Ronald E. Frank
University of Pennsylvania

Paul E. Green
University of Pennsylvania

QUANTITATIVE
METHODS
IN MARKETING

Prentice-Hall, Inc., Englewood Cliffs, New Jersey

QUANTITATIVE METHODS IN MARKETING
Frank and Green

FOUNDATIONS OF MARKETING SERIES

Current printing (last digit):

11   10   9   8   7   6   5   4

PRENTICE-HALL INTERNATIONAL, INC.   *London*
PRENTICE-HALL OF AUSTRALIA, PTY. LTD.   *Sydney*
PRENTICE-HALL OF CANADA, LTD.   *Toronto*
PRENTICE-HALL OF INDIA PRIVATE LTD.   *New Delhi*
PRENTICE-HALL OF JAPAN, INC.   *Tokyo*

The Foundations of Marketing is a series of authoritative and concise books prepared to serve the need for teaching materials incorporating the results of recent research and developments in the study and practice of marketing. The structure of the series—its flexibility within unity of purpose—enables the teacher to construct a complete basic marketing course, adjustable to a level of rigor of the teacher's choosing. Certain

Foundations
of Marketing Series

or all books can be combined to accomplish individual course objectives. Individual books are self-contained, reasonably complete treatments of the fundamental changes taking place in their areas. Students have the benefits of being introduced to the managerial approach to the field and to the socioeconomic process of marketing by authorities actively engaged in study and research in each field.

An overview of the series and of the managerial approach to marketing is provided by

Marketing: Strategy and Functions

Four books treat important aspects of scientific methodology and decision making in marketing:

Consumer Behavior
Marketing Management and the Social Sciences
Men, Motives, and Markets
Quantitative Methods in Marketing

Key policy areas of marketing are covered in

Pricing and Marketing Strategy
Product Policy
Promotion: A Behavioral View
Channel Management
Physical Distribution

Important environmental areas in marketing are emphasized in

International Marketing
Marketing and Public Policy
Marketing in the Canadian Environment

All books may profitably use as supplements

Cases in Marketing Management
Advanced Cases in Marketing Management

It is hoped that the series will stimulate independent and intelligent thought about the central issues of marketing analysis and policy and that readers will find the books useful guides to a creative and disciplined approach to meeting complex and changing marketing problems.

EUGENE J. KELLEY, *Editor*

Parts of Chapter 2 are reprinted from Paul E. Green and Donald S. Tull's "Bayesian Statistics in Marketing Research," *Applied Statistics,* XV (November 1966), 173–90. Part of Chapter 3 is reprinted from Ronald E. Frank and Paul E. Green's *A Manager's Guide to Marketing Research* (New York: John Wiley & Sons, Inc., 1967), pp. 68–94. And sections of Chapter 5 are reprinted from Paul E. Green and Donald S. Tull's *Research for Marketing Decisions* (Englewood Cliffs, N. J.: Prentice-Hall, Inc., 1966), *passim*.

Contents

QUANTITATIVE METHODS IN MARKETING

1

From the firm's viewpoint, the primary justification for any form of marketing analysis is to reduce the costs of error in making decisions. Decision making implies the existence of a goal (or goals) as well as a set of alternatives as a basis for choice. The decision-making process consists of the following steps: (1) problem recognition and formulation, including the specification of goals; (2) specification of alternative courses of action; (3) identification of key uncertainties; (4) collection of relevant data; (5)

The Role
of
Quantitative Techniques

estimation of the value of alternative courses of action; and (6) implementation of the alternative chosen. The effectiveness of a firm's decision-making activity can be looked upon as the result of how well each of these steps is performed.

This text is concerned with the contribution that quantitative techniques can make to decision making in marketing. Primary emphasis is placed on the *conceptual* nature of the techniques—not on their computational aspects or on the wide variety of hypothesis-testing and estimation procedures that are encountered in applied statistics courses. Although numerical illustrations are used quite liberally in places, their purpose is to illuminate the concepts rather than to develop the reader's computational proficiency. Our objective (and hope) has been to provide an *intermediate-level critical examination of selected techniques while paying major attention to marketing applications.*

THE ROLE OF QUANTITATIVE TECHNIQUES

As the marketing profession has developed, marketing researchers, corporate planners, operations researchers, and other staff specialists have been called upon to contribute to the solution of increasingly complex problems. This trend, in turn, has led to the need for finding better ways to formulate and test explicit models of both the executive decision-making process and customer and

1

distributor behavior. (By the term *model* we mean a simplified representation, often in terms of a mathematical, statistical, or logical set of relationships, of some aspect or aspects of human behavior or of a physical system.)

The principal, though not the sole, impact of model building on the decision-making process has been to provide improved means for evaluating the effects of alternative courses of action (step 5 above). But the process of formulating such a model forces both the decision maker and researcher to make its assumptions explicit and to trace out the logical consequences implied by the assertions made during the first three steps of the decision-making process.

This is not to say, however, that quantitative techniques have contributed only to the formulation of problems and the evaluation of alternative courses of action. In the words of Wroe Alderson:

> Quantitative models are not the purely logical models of economic theory in which the only results to be obtained are inferences drawn from the structure of the model itself. The very term "quantitative model" suggests the combination of empirical data with the logical structure of the system which the model represents. Instead of perpetuating the argument between the fact finders and the logicians the new emphasis on explicit quantitative models holds out the hope that these separate contributions can now be successfully integrated. In fact, the quantitative models which are now coming into use should lead to improvements in both the logic and the data of marketing analysis.[1]

A well-formulated decision problem is one of the best guides, if not *the* best guide, to the collection of relevant data in the decision-making process (step 4) that either the researcher or decision maker is apt to find.

Ideally one would like to possess a model (or a set of models) to be used as a basis for *prescribing* which of a set of alternatives a decision maker should choose, given the problem he faces. If this ideal were, in fact, achieved, the contribution of model building and quantitative techniques to the decision-making process would be quite direct and unambiguous. Management scientists have done a considerable amount of work on the development of prescriptive models; numerous models have been developed for handling inventory, allocation, queuing, sequencing, replacement, and search problems, to name only a few. However, the development of these models has thus far had relatively little impact on decision-making *behavior*, primarily because the development of a prescriptive model assumes that one is able to *describe*, in considerable detail, the situation that is being modeled. It is useful to think of a *prescriptive* model as being composed of a number of *descriptive* components.

---

[1] In Ronald E. Frank, Alfred A. Kuehn, and William F. Massy, *Quantitative Techniques in Marketing Analysis* (Homewood, Ill.: Richard D. Irwin, Inc., 1962), p. xv.

For example, if one wanted to construct a prescriptive model to determine the optimal inventory level for a firm, he would need information as to the nature of at least two descriptive models: (1) one that would provide a description of the relationship between costs that *increase* as inventory increases (such as storage, obsolescence, deterioration, insurance, taxes) and the quantity of inventory held; and (2) one that would provide a description of the relationship between costs that *decrease* as inventory increases (such as shortage costs, production costs, setup and take-down costs) and the quantity of inventory held. These two descriptive models would then be combined to arrive at a prescriptive model.

One can specify the nature of these descriptive relationships in at least two ways short of going out and attempting to measure them:

> 1. The "Let us assume a response function" method. When done well, this approach begins with a search for behavioral data that are available in the literature and from the cooperating firm. Then the analyst subjectively integrates his findings into a set of mathematical formulations which he hopes will provide a reasonable approximation to the relevant behavioral (descriptive) phenomena upon which operations analysis must be based. Unfortunately, some published "decision-making models" fail even to indicate that a comprehensive search for relevant behavioral materials has been undertaken prior to making assumptions about the form of the model.
>
> 2. The "Let management assume a response function" method. Here the analyst admits at the outset of his study that he lacks the detailed knowledge that is needed to make effective predictions. Rather than employing what may be essentially *ad hoc* assumptions, he asks management to assist him in his task by suggesting the nature of market responses that are likely to ensue if the firm adopts a given strategy. The analyst interprets these comments—perhaps by employing mathematical or probabilistic methods—and uses them as the behavioral components of his normative model. This approach is often used in operations research studies based on Bayesian decision theory.

Unfortunately, many prescriptive models go no further than this. It is our opinion that the major contribution of quantitative techniques, given the present state of the art of model building, is their use to develop descriptive models based on live data rather than on managers' or researchers' hunches alone. Thus, our primary, though not exclusive, focus in this volume is on measurement and testing. The reason for this is succinctly stated by Martin Starr: "Until we have sufficient relevant information—converted into realistic distributions and parameters—our simulation models [as well as other types of models] of consumer behavior will remain abstractions, fascinating to those who conceive them, fantastic to those who misconstrue them, frustrating to those who would use them." [2]

[2] "Computers: The Marketing Laboratory," in Peter Langhoff, ed., *Models, Measurement, and Marketing* (Englewood Cliffs, N. J.: Prentice-Hall, Inc., 1965), p. 79.

Our state of descriptive knowledge is sufficiently limited, however, to prevent us from developing prescriptive models in which a large proportion of the descriptive components have been empirically tested. With this limitation in mind, we have chosen *not* to cover a broad range of standard optimization models. Excellent accounts of these works are available elsewhere.[3] We have chosen instead to focus our attention on those techniques (multivariate analysis and experimental design) that have been primarily used as a basis for developing and testing *descriptive* models. We have included simulation as a topic not only because it is a tool for model development and testing but because we believe that it is one of the few quantitative techniques capable of handling the complexities involved in ultimately integrating the many descriptive models required to build a "data-based" prescriptive model of a complex business situation.

The only exception to the aforementioned rationale for choosing textual material is the chapter on Bayesian decision theory (Chapter 2). We included it because we feel (in spite of its low rate of "real" applications in marketing thus far) that it makes available for the first time a logically consistent methodology that can simultaneously:

1. Help to structure the principal alternatives among which a decision is to be made.
2. Formally incorporate the economics of a decision problem and provide a consistent, formal technique for combining an executive's prior judgments about the nature of his environment with the results of research findings about that environment.
3. Deal explicitly with the problem of uncertainty associated with the consequences of different managerial actions and with the reliability and relevance of alternative sources of information.

Chapter 2 thus provides a general framework within which the content of succeeding chapters can be placed. That is, the "output" of various experimental and observational investigations—as well as simulation—may be viewed as a special type of information about the decision maker's environment or the consequences associated with various courses of action.

Chapter 3 discusses the use of experimental procedures as a basis for evaluating the effects of different components of a firm's marketing program. In experimentation, alternative strategies, for example, are actually tried out on a small scale in order to determine the responses of customers or middlemen. Not long ago experimental procedures were looked upon as "impractical" or academic. Now their use in marketing has become increasingly widespread.

---

[3] For example, see Russell L. Ackoff and Patrick Rivett, *A Manager's Guide to Operations Research* (New York: John Wiley & Sons, Inc., 1963), and C. West Churchman, Russell L. Ackoff, and E. Leonard Arnoff, *Introduction to Operations Research* (New York: John Wiley & Sons, Inc., 1957).

Next, in Chapter 4, we discuss a broad range of multivariate statistical techniques that are used primarily as a basis for analyzing nonexperimental (observational) data. With these tools one can look simultaneously at the effects of a reasonably large number of factors on customer, market, or distributor behavior—an especially important characteristic, since most problems that confront marketing management involve assessing the effects of a large number of factors at once, and without the aid of some type of formal analytical procedure most of us find it difficult to think about the relationships of two or three variables at once, let alone ten, fifteen, or fifty.

In Chapter 5 we discuss the principal types of simulation models that have been developed for dealing with problems such as media scheduling and physical distribution. Often the complexity of marketing problems goes beyond our ability to formulate a formal *analytical* model. Simulation provides a flexible approach to model construction that permits the manipulation of a model even when it cannot be "solved" in analytical form; hence in this chapter we emphasize simulation techniques as a flexible approach to marketing problem formulation and "solution."

The concluding chapter of the book provides a brief look at things to come in the application of quantitative tools to marketing problems.

Part Two

TYPES OF QUANTITATIVE TECHNIQUES

2

THE DOMAIN OF DECISION MAKING

Over the last decade a conceptual viewpoint and body of techniques —statistical decision theory—has been developed and applied on a limited basis to business problem solving. The purpose of this chapter is to introduce the major concepts underlying this approach and

Bayesian Decision Theory and Marketing Analysis

to describe their relevance to the analysis of marketing problems. In a very real sense the subject of this whole book is decision making, or at least that part of decision making concerned with quantitative techniques that can be helpful in making "better" marketing decisions. Statistical decision theory is only part of the decision-making process, but it is a significant one. Other approaches (and other disciplines) have been used to study how people should—or actually do—make decisions. Figure 2-1 shows one way of classifying the domain of decision making. By following through this classification we shall be able to see where *Bayesian theory*—a name given to statistical decision theory because of its frequent (though not necessary) use of a theorem developed by an eighteenth century clergyman, Thomas Bayes—fits into the over-all framework. (The reader should note that the tree diagram has been used only for ease of illustration; the descriptors are not hierarchical.)

Prescription versus Description

Looking at the first set of branches in Figure 2-1, we note that decisions can be studied from either a prescriptive or descriptive viewpoint. Prescriptive (or normative) science is concerned with how people *should* make decisions, whereas descriptive (or positive) science is concerned with how people *do* make decisions. To illustrate, the economist or operations researcher is largely concerned with prescribing; that is, his ultimate objective usually is to make some recommendation to the decision maker for improving his decisions. The psychologist or sociologist, on the other hand, is typically concerned with describing how people do, in fact, make decisions.

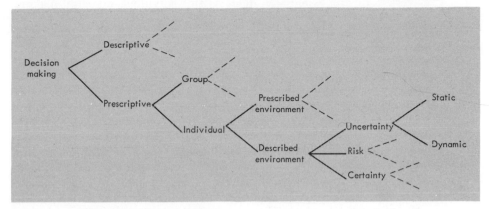

FIG. 2-1 A classification of decision making.

It should be remembered, though, that all recommendations presuppose some description of the environment in which the decision is to take place. If the operations researcher, economist, or marketing analyst is not also concerned with description, his recommendations may lead to exceedingly poor results. Moreover, the behavioral scientist may also be interested in prescription; a case in point is the psychiatrist who is engaged in psychotherapy. Thus, prescriptive science uses the results of descriptive science in order to make recommendations, and prescriptive models can be used descriptively as first approximations of how people really behave. The distinction between the two approaches is mainly one of intent rather than method.

Bayesian decision theory is primarily prescriptive; that is, it is concerned with how a consistent decision maker should choose courses of action. As we shall see later, however, the model can be and has been used to study how people actually make choices.

Individual versus Group Decision Making

A second distinction in the domain of decision making is that between individual and group behavior. The distinction rests less on the number of individuals involved than on the consistency of the group's objectives, beliefs, and attitudes toward risk. If we can assume a single goal-belief-risk structure, we are dealing with individual decision making, regardless of the number of individuals involved. On the other hand, if any of these components varies among the individuals constituting the decision-making group, we are coping with group choice making. We know relatively little about the latter category that is useful for prescriptive science. Study of group decision making requires knowledge of value trade-offs, conflict resolution, persuasion, threat, bluffing, and a variety of other characteristics associated with interpersonal relations; it has largely been the province of the political scientist, the organization theorist, and the lawyer.

Bayesian theory essentially deals with individual decision making, where *individual* means an entity possessing a consistent set of objectives, beliefs, and attitudes toward risk (whether or not more than one person is involved).

The Problem's Environment

All decisions must, of course, be made in some kind of environmental context, and a third distinction in the domain of decision making concerns ways of viewing the environment. There are two basic ways, which can be labeled descriptive and prescriptive. In the former view, the decision maker attempts to appraise the likelihood that various events will occur; he assumes that the environment can be described in terms of a set of "states of nature" which affect the outcome of alternative courses of action; he attempts to describe these possible states of nature and to assign chances of their occurrence. If the environment includes "hostile" components—i.e., competitors, his job is to predict what they *will* do, not what they should do under some set assumptions about their rationality.

The other way of viewing the environment—prescriptively—is to make assumptions about the rationality of the opponents—competitors—who exist in it, and to base one's actions upon these assumptions on the basis of the mathematics of "game theory." [1] The use of game theory guarantees the decision maker a certain minimum payoff if his competitor behaves on the basis of the rationality that it assumes him to have. If the competitor behaves in a different way, the decision maker's payoff can be greater.

Bayesian theory views the environment descriptively, and treats the possible actions of opponents just as it treats other unknown events, rather than in the special way that constitutes the subject of game theory.

Information about the Environment

Decisions can also be classified according to the amount of knowledge the decision maker has of his environment. If he has perfect knowledge, he makes his decisions under conditions of *certainty*. For example, if he knew the exact response of sales to alternative levels of advertising, he could determine by appropriate computation the exact advertising expenditure that without fail would yield some designated level of sales.

If, on the other hand, he does not know the exact response of sales to different levels of advertising but knows the probability of various re-

---

[1] See John D. Williams, *The Compleat Strategyst*, rev. ed. (New York: McGraw-Hill Book Company, 1965), and John Von Neumann and Oskar Morgenstern, *Theory of Games and Economic Behavior*, 3rd ed. (New York: John Wiley & Sons, Inc., 1964; a Science Editions paperback). In our illustration we are referring specifically to two-person constant-sum games.

sponses, he must make his decisions under conditions of *risk*. He is assumed to choose that action which on the average will lead to some "best" level of return.

In most real-world marketing problems, one cannot reasonably assume even "known" probability distributions over alternative states of nature. In this most realistic but most difficult situation, one must make decisions under conditions of *uncertainty*. Bayesian decision theory is usually placed in this third category, along with some other procedures (such as maximin, minimax regret) which establish normative procedures for making decisions when probability distributions are not "known."[2]

Static versus Dynamic Decisions

In some marketing situations, a problem is encountered, an alternative is chosen, an outcome occurs, and the problem is "resolved." Much current theory has been concerned with this "one-shot," or *static*, decision making. Bayesian theory can deal with it, but also with *dynamic*, or *sequential*, decision making, in which the outcome of a previous decision may affect subsequent decisions. In this latter event, the decision maker plans a strategy of interrelated actions (which may include the gathering of information) for reacting to alternative events in the future.[3]

The Decision Process

The Bayesian approach, then, is concerned with either static or dynamic decisions; it prescribes for individual choices made under conditions of uncertainty about alternative descriptions of a problem's environment. The decision *process*, however, involves more than just choice. It is typified by: (1) problem recognition and formulation; (2) search for courses of action; (3) choice; and (4) implementation and control of the selected alternative.[4] Of course, choice making occurs at all these steps, and at others as well: in the formulation of courses of action; in the establishment of measures of the effectiveness of decisions; in the description of alternate states of nature, etc. Further, all these steps are highly interrelated; the formulation of the problem, for instance, may undergo more or less continuous modification as the other steps are followed through.

In the section that follows, we shall examine a hypothetical marketing problem, concentrating on the actual choice of alternate courses of action but recognizing that this is only one step in the problem-solving process.

---

[2] A discussion of these alternative choice models may be found in Wroe Alderson and Paul E. Green, *Planning and Problem Solving in Marketing* (Homewood, Ill.: Richard D. Irwin, Inc., 1964).

[3] See Ward Edwards, "Dynamic Decision Theory and Probabilistic Information Processing, *Human Factors*, VI (April 1962), 59–73.

[4] This classification is made by Herbert A. Simon in *Models of Man* (New York: John Wiley & Sons, Inc., 1957).

THE BAYESIAN APPROACH

In preceding paragraphs we have tried to show where Bayesian decision theory fits into a general schema of decision making. Our task now is to explain the approach in some detail and (by simplified numerical examples) to illustrate its application. As indicated earlier, Bayesian theory is concerned with rational choice behavior—that is, with behavior that is consistent with the assumptions underlying the theory. These assumptions will become apparent as we describe an illustrative problem.

Suppose the marketing manager of the Digitalis Drug Company has to decide whether to launch an intensive promotional campaign in behalf of his firm's most profitable product, Cheery, a toothpaste that contains the magic ingredient NaCl. If the firm's chief competitor, the Dental Frost Company, decides to launch *its* new toothpaste, Whitey, during the next quarter, Digitalis' marketing manager feels that the ad campaign should be launched immediately in order to lessen the impact of Whitey's introduction on Cheery's market share. If Dental Frost does not introduce Whitey, however, the campaign is assumed not to be needed, inasmuch as Cheery's sales are satisfactory.

The marketing manager, through consultation with his advertising and marketing research manager, next estimates the net financial payoffs to the firm under various action-state combinations. The structure of the problem is shown in Table 2-1. Looking at the table we first note that the

TABLE 2-1 Decision Table—Illustrative Problem (net financial payoffs in millions of dollars)

Acts	S_1: Whitey enters market	S_2: Whitey does not enter market
A_1: Launch campaign	8	7
A_2: Do not launch campaign	2	10

"best of all possible worlds" for Digitalis would occur if act A_2 were chosen and Whitey toothpaste were not introduced. Under this set of circumstances no additional out-of-pocket costs need be incurred for advertising (which is assumed to be unprofitable, on balance), Cheery's market share would not be adversely affected, and the firm would make $10 million in profits. The next best situation would be to launch the campaign and find (later) that Whitey was introduced. In this case the advertising would help to reduce Cheery's loss in market share, but, on balance, only $8 million in profits would be produced.

If A_1 is taken and S_2 occurs, then Digitalis' additional advertising is essentially wasted, since we assume, on balance, that profit on additional sales is not sufficient to recoup the incremental cost of the additional advertising; thus, only $7 million in profits would occur. Finally, if A_2 is taken and S_1 occurs, the financial penalty is extreme; only $2 million in profits would be earned. In this case Whitey is assumed to capture a significant enough share of the market to reduce Digitalis' profits by $8 million, as compared to the outcome expected under the A_2, S_2 situation.

Opportunity Losses

Notice that in Table 2-1 all entries are expressed in terms of profits or, more generally, "payoffs." Another way of looking at the problem, common in decision theory, is to work with *opportunity losses*, which concern *differential* payoffs, in which the value of a specific outcome is compared to the value of the best outcome possible, given a particular state of nature. For example, if S_1 were to occur, the best act is A_1, for no opportunity loss is suffered. If A_2 were taken under these conditions, the firm would suffer an opportunity loss of $6 million, since only $2 million profit would be made, rather than $8 million. Similarly, if S_2 were to occur, the best act is A_2; an opportunity loss of $3 million would be suffered if A_1 were taken.

The payoffs of Table 2-1 thus can be translated into the opportunity losses shown in Table 2-2. (Note that opportunity losses are never negative.) As we shall show later on when we discuss choice criteria, maximizing the average payoff (using the data of Table 2-1) is equivalent to

TABLE 2-2   Opportunity Loss Table—Illustrative Problem

Acts	S_1: Whitey enters market	S_2: Whitey does not enter market
A_1: Launch campaign	0	3
A_2: Do not launch campaign	6	0

minimizing the average loss (using the data of Table 2-2). We shall work with opportunity losses merely to simplify the computations.

Several questions remain unanswered in our description of this illustrative problem. For example, why only two courses of action and two states of nature? Can Digitalis procure additional information regarding its competitor's plans? For what period of time should financial measures be computed? Are financial outcomes the only relevant measure of effectiveness? These questions are important in the structuring of real problems, and we shall return to them in the section devoted to applications of the Bayesian approach.

For purposes of illustration, however, assume that the data of Table 2-1 (and the derivation data of Table 2-2) are relevant. Obviously the marketing manager would like to choose the course of action that would lead to the lowest opportunity loss. Unfortunately, he cannot *control the* occurrence of the states of nature (S_1 or S_2) nor can he even *predict* which event will actually occur.

Prior Analysis

Suppose, however, that the sales manager, through a variety of "marketing intelligence" sources (salesmen's comments, trade announcements, test market reports), believes that there is an 80 per cent chance that the Dental Frost Company *will* introduce Whitey in the next quarter and, conversely, a 20 per cent chance that it will not. With this information, he can consider using the Bayesian choice criterion: *"Choose that course of action which, on the average, leads to the best payoff."* In this illustration the manager would like to keep average opportunity loss to a minimum; "best" in this case is minimum average loss. To find the expected (average) loss, *EL*, of each act, we merely multiply the conditional losses (conditional, that is, upon the occurrence of state of nature S_1 or S_2) by the manager's prior beliefs, expressed as probabilities, that each state will occur:

$$EL\,(A_1) = 0.8\,(0) + 0.2\,(3) = \$0.6 \text{ million}$$

$$EL\,(A_2) = 0.8\,(6) + 0.2\,(0) = \$4.8 \text{ million}$$

Using this criterion for choice, the manager should choose act A_1—that is, "launch the campaign," inasmuch as it carries the lower expected (opportunity) loss.

We should mention, however, that minimizing expected loss (or, equivalently,[5] maximizing expected payoff) is not a *choice criterion* unique to the Bayesian approach. "Decision making under conditions of risk" (described earlier) uses the same criterion. The difference is that in the latter case the probabilities are assumed to be "known," while in the former they can only be estimated subjectively. The Bayesian approach can be used for decision making under conditions of risk by assuming that *all* probabilities are subjective but that some—for example, the probability of drawing a spade from a well-shuffled bridge deck—are more generally agreed upon than others. Without debating this issue, we can see that minimizing expected loss (or maximizing expected payoff) is a rather general criterion for choice when outcomes are not known with certainty but when probabilities—either subjective or objective—can be assigned to the possible states of nature.

A second consideration of interest concerns the *precision* required in

---

[5] The reader may convince himself that the absolute difference between the expected losses of A_1 and A_2 (\$4.2 million) equals the absolute difference between the expected payoffs using the data of Table 2-1. In this latter case the criterion would involve choosing that act with *maximum* expected payoff. In either case the criteria lead to the same selection—A_1 in this illustration.

probability specification. In terms of the illustrative problem, one might wonder how small the probability assigned to S_1 could be before the decision is reversed from A_1 to A_2. This "indifference" probability may be found by equating the expected losses of the two acts, as follows:

Where

$$P_1 = \text{the probability of state } S_1$$
$$(1 - P_1) = \text{the probability of state } S_2$$

$$EL(A_1) = EL(A_2)$$
$$P_1(0) + (1 - P_1)(3) = P_1(6) + (1 - P_1)(0)$$
$$3 - 3P_1 = 6\,P_1$$
$$9P_1 = 3$$
$$P_1 = \frac{1}{3}; \ (1 - P_1) = \frac{2}{3}$$

Thus, if P_1 is greater than $\frac{1}{3}$, A_1 leads to a lower expected loss than act A_2. If P_1 is less than $\frac{1}{3}$, A_2 leads to a lower expected loss. The decision maker is only required, then, to estimate whether the probability is less than (or greater than) the "indifference" value of $\frac{1}{3}$.

In summary, in prior analysis it is assumed that the decision maker can list a relevant set of mutually exclusive, collectively exhaustive courses of action and states of nature. Furthermore, he can determine the payoffs associated with each act-state combination and his beliefs—expressed as numerical probabilities—about the likelihood that each state will occur. The choice criterion involves selection of that course of action which leads to the lowest expected loss (or highest expected payoff, if the outcomes are expressed as conditional gains).

Extensive Form Analysis—Bayes' Theorem

Up to this point we have not discussed the "Bayesian" part of the approach. Bayesian theory also prescribes how prior probability judgments *should be modified* when new information is made available to the decision maker. Suppose we return to the illustrative problem. We now assume that the sales manager's wife's nephew is a junior executive in the competing firm. While not privy to all of Dental Frost's strategic information, the nephew, on past occasions, has provided (unfortunately, fallible) opinions about the strategic moves of his company. We assume that if he were contacted surreptitiously, he would reply either "We'll market," "We'll not market," or "I don't know." On the basis of past performance, the marketing manager of Digitalis evaluates the probabilities relating his wife's nephew's statements to the true (forthcoming) events, as shown in Table 2-3.

The figures in Table 2-3 are conditional probabilities $P(Z_i|S_j)$ that specific statements—Z_1, Z_2, or Z_3—will be made given the true situation—S_1 or S_2. Notice that the nephew's statements are fallible. That is, if S_1 is really the case, there is only a 90 per cent chance that the nephew will so indicate by saying "We'll market"; 5 per cent of the time he will say

TABLE 2-3   Conditional Probabilities of Nephew's
Statements, Given Each State of Nature

Nephew's statements	S_1: Whitey enters market	S_2: Whitey does not enter market
Z_1: "We'll market"	0.90	0.60
Z_2: "We'll not market"	0.05	0.30
Z_3: "I don't know"	0.05	0.10
	1.00	1.00

"We'll not market" and 5 per cent of the time he will say "I don't know." (In these latter instances he will not report the event correctly.) The conditional probabilities given S_2 are interpreted analogously.

Suppose the nephew is contacted and he replies "We'll market." We know that this message could be received under either S_1 or S_2 conditions. Given this piece of new information, what should the manager do? More generally, what should the manager do, given each of the three possible replies of the nephew? In order to answer these questions, recourse is made to Bayes' theorem. What we desire are the *posterior* probabilities $P(S_1|Z_i)$ and $P(S_2|Z_i)$, which are conditional upon the (assumed) known reply of the nephew. These probabilities are computed in Table 2-4.

TABLE 2-4   Calculation of Posterior Probabilities

(1) Nephew's statements	(2) Joint probabilities $P(S_1) \cdot P(Z_i|S_1)$	(3) Joint probabilities $P(S_2) \cdot P(Z_i|S_2)$	(4) Marginal probabilities $P(Z_i)$	(5) Posterior probabilities $P(S_1|Z_i)$	(6) Posterior probabilities $P(S_2|Z_i)$
Z_1	0.72	0.12	0.84	0.86	0.14
Z_2	0.04	0.06	0.10	0.40	0.60
Z_3	0.04	0.02	0.06	0.67	0.33
$P(S_j)$	0.80	0.20	1.00		

We first compute the joint probabilities $P(S_j) \cdot P(Z_i|S_j)$. For example, the probability that Whitey will enter the market *and* the nephew will say "We'll market" is

$$P(S_1) \cdot P(Z_1|S_1) = 0.8 \,(0.9) = 0.72$$

We note that all acquired information for Table 2-4 is obtainable from Table 2-3 and the sales manager's prior probabilities of 0.8 and 0.2 assigned to the occurrence of S_1 and S_2, respectively. We compute all appropriate joint probabilities shown in columns 2 and 3 in similar fashion. Notice (since we require that S_j be exclusive and exhaustive) that these probabilities sum to the marginal totals, Z_i, shown in column 4.

Now suppose that Z_1 has been observed and we are required to find the posterior probabilities $P(S_1|Z_1)$ and $P(S_2|Z_1)$. We need only ask: "Given Z_1, what is the probability that S_1 is true?" This probability is:

$$P(S_1|Z_1) = \frac{0.72}{0.84} = 0.86$$

Similarly, the probability of S_2 conditional upon the occurrence of Z_1 is:

$$P(S_2|Z_1) = \frac{0.12}{0.84} = 0.14$$

Bayes' theorem formalizes this procedure by means of the following formula (illustrated for the first case):

$$P(S_1|Z_1) = \frac{P(S_1) \cdot P(Z_1|S_1)}{\sum_{j=1}^{2} P(S_j) \cdot P(Z_1|S_j)}$$

$$= \frac{0.8 \times 0.9}{(0.8 \times 0.9) + (0.6 \times 0.2)}$$

$$= 0.86$$

Note that this is just another way of expressing conditional probability—this time, *the probability of a state of nature, conditional upon the appearance of some sample event.*

We are now ready to evaluate what the manager should do, conditional upon each of the possible statements the nephew can make. Figure 2-2 summarizes this evaluation in tree diagram form. In the figure *all* reactions to the nephew's statements have been worked out in extensive form. For example, if Z_1 is indicated, the appropriate posterior probabilities are 0.86 and 0.14 for S_1 and S_2, respectively. Computing expected losses for each act under this set of revised probabilities indicates that A_1, with an expected loss of $0.42 million, is more favorable than A_2, with an expected loss of $5.16 million. Thus, *if* the nephew were to indicate Z_1, the sales manager should choose A_1 and launch the campaign. This is indicated in the diagram by blocking off act A_2 with a double slash.

When we examine, step by step, the other possible outcomes (Z_2 and Z_3) we find that in *each* case act A_1 should be chosen. *But this is what the sales manager was planning to do anyway.* We merely note at this point that the nephew's responses do *not* appear to be yielding any "information" in the sense of changing what the sales manager would do *in the absence* of the nephew's report.

We shall return to this illustration after discussing Bayesian analysis in "normal" form (in which Bayes' theorem is not used). At this point, how-

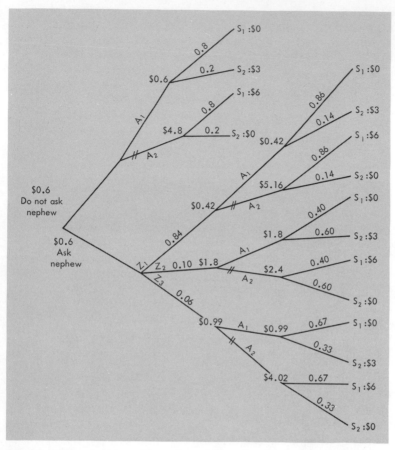

FIG. 2-2 Value of prior analysis versus value of using nephew's service (dollar entries in millions).

ever, we can summarize the extensive form of Bayesian analysis by indicating that it prescribes what the manager should do, given every possible event, Z_i. Acts are still selected on the basis of minimizing expected loss, but now using *posterior* probabilities, incorporating the sample outcomes Z_i. Otherwise, this part of the procedure is equivalent to prior analysis. We have merely *updated* the prior probabilities by incorporating the "information" provided by the nephew.

Normal Form Analysis

Bayesian analysis does not always require the use of Bayes' theorem in the selection of appropriate strategies. In the so-called "normal form" analysis, equivalent results are obtained without recourse to the theorem. Suppose we return to our numerical illustration and now assume that we would like to lay out *in advance* all possible strategies for reacting to the nephew's statements. Table 2-5 lists all of these pos-

TABLE 2-5   Possible Strategies Given Nephew's
Statements

Strategies	Z_1: "We'll market"	Z_2: "We'll not market"	Z_3: "I don't know"
s_1	A_1	A_1	A_1
s_2	A_1	A_1	A_2
s_3	A_1	A_2	A_1
s_4	A_1	A_2	A_2
s_5	A_2	A_1	A_1
s_6	A_2	A_1	A_2
s_7	A_2	A_2	A_1
s_8	A_2	A_2	A_2

sibilities. We note that each s_i represents a "recipe" for reacting to each possible statement made by the nephew. Our task is to evaluate the *conditional* expected loss, *CEL*, associated with each *strategy*, given that S_1 and S_2, respectively, are true. If, for example, we adopt strategy s_1 under S_1 conditions, our conditional expected loss will be:

$$CEL(s_1|S_1) = 0.9\,(0) + 0.05\,(0) + 0.05\,(0)$$
$$= \$0 \text{ million}$$

The entries on the right side of the equation are obtained from Tables 2-2 and 2-3. That is, assuming A_1 is *always* taken, the conditional loss is zero if S_1 occurs. Similarly, under S_2 conditions:

$$CEL\,(s_1|S_2) = 0.6\,(3) + 0.3\,(3) + 0.1\,(3)$$
$$= \$3 \text{ million}$$

For strategy s_2 we have:

$$CEL\,(s_2|S_1) = 0.9\,(0) + 0.05\,(0) + 0.05\,(6)$$
$$= \$0.3 \text{ million}$$

$$CEL\,(s_2|S_2) = 0.6\,(3) + 0.3\,(3) + 0.1\,(0)$$
$$= \$2.7 \text{ million}$$

Conditional expected losses for the other six strategies are shown in Table 2-6 and are plotted in Figure 2-3.

In Figure 2-3 a dotted line connects the points represented by s_1, s_3, s_4 and s_8; note that points s_2, s_5, s_6 and s_7 all lie *above* this boundary. These latter strategies are called *inadmissible* or *dominated*, since some combination of s_1, s_3, s_4 or s_8 will always lead to a lower average loss than they will. For example, suppose a mixture of s_1 and s_3 were developed in

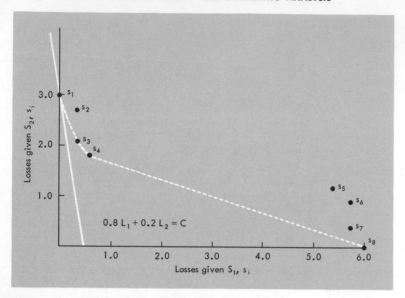

FIG. 2-3 Conditional expected losses (normal form analysis).

TABLE 2-6 Conditional Expected Losses of Possible Strategies s_i
(in millions of dollars)

States	s_1	s_2	s_3	s_4	s_5	s_6	s_7	s_8
S_1	0	0.3	0.3	0.6	5.4	5.7	5.7	6.0
S_2	3.0	2.7	2.1	1.8	1.2	0.9	0.3	0

which each would be taken half the time (using some kind of randomizing device). The average loss of this "mixed" strategy would be:

$$\text{Given } S_1: 0.5(0) + 0.5(0.3) = \$0.15 \text{ million}$$

$$\text{Given } S_2: 0.5(3.0) + 0.5(2.1) = \$2.55 \text{ million}$$

Under either state of nature this mixture is preferable to s_2. It and any other mixture of s_1 and s_3 fall on the line connecting the two points and hence dominate s_2.

In general, *every* admissible strategy is a Bayes strategy for some set of prior probabilities, and its expected loss is conditional upon which state occurs. In the illustrative problem these probabilities are 0.8 and 0.2 for S_1 and S_2, respectively. We can move a straight line

$$0.8 L_1 + 0.2 L_2 = C$$

out from the origin until it just touches a point on the lower boundary of the (convex) set of points. Relative to *this* set of prior probabilities the line touches the figure at point s_1. This agrees with the results of the extensive form analysis. *Regardless* of the nephew's statement, the marketing manager should take action A_1, that is, launch the campaign. Now we can derive the unconditional expected losses for each of the admissible (pure) strategies. The unconditional expected loss of s_1, for example, is:

$$0.8(0) + 0.2(3) = \$0.6 \text{ million}$$

Computation of the losses for the remaining strategies is handled analogously: $s_2 = \$0.66$ million; $s_4 = \$0.84$ million; and $s_8 = \$4.80$ million. (Notice that the loss of s_1 is the lowest of the group.)

In summary, extensive form and normal form analysis produce equivalent results. Selection of the appropriate mode of analysis is based more on pragmatic than on theoretical grounds.[6] In general, the extensive form permits one to cross bridges one at a time by updating prior probabilities on the basis of sample outcomes that *actually* occur, rather than for all those that *could* occur. As we shall see in the next section, however, in many situations this gain is illusory since the major question usually is whether the data should be collected in the first place.

Preposterior Analysis—Extensive Form

We continue our discussion of the problems facing the marketing manager of the Digitalis Drug Company. We have already indicated what he should do given only the prior probabilities (he should take action A_1). We have also seen what he should do if he seeks his wife's nephew's advice (he should take action A_1 no matter what the nephew replies). Now we add two additional considerations to the analysis. First, we assume that the nephew wishes to charge \$10,000 for supplying the marketing intelligence report, as described earlier; and second, we assume that the sales manager of Digitalis has access to a "perfect" intelligence service that will tell him the true state of nature *without error*. This professional "spy" charges the comparatively large fee of \$500,000 for his service. The sales manager thus has three options:

1. Purchase neither intelligence service and proceed on the basis of of prior information alone.
2. Purchase the "amateur" service provided by the nephew.
3. Purchase the "professional" service which provides perfect information (at a higher cost).

We have already evaluated the first option. Referring to Figure 2-2, we see that on the basis of a prior analysis, the best act to take is A_1, which yields the minimum loss of \$0.6 million.

[6] An illustration of normal form analysis may be found in Chapter 9 of Paul E. Green and Donald S. Tull, *Research for Marketing Decisions* (Englewood Cliffs, N. J.: Prentice-Hall, Inc., 1966).

It is also easy to evaluate the nephew's service. Since the nephew's replies have *no potential for changing the course of action* (in this case, A_1) that would be taken in the absence of his information, we would guess that his service is not worth *any* additional outlay. That this is indeed the case can be verified from Figure 2-2.

Looking at the branch labeled "Ask nephew" we see that the marginal probabilities for obtaining sample outcomes Z_1, Z_2 and Z_3 are 0.84, 0.1, and 0.06, respectively. Furthermore, we have already computed the (conditional) expected loss associated with taking the best act (in this case, always A_1), given each sample outcome. These losses are $0.42, $1.8, and $0.99 million, respectively, for Z_1, Z_2, and Z_3. But these losses are still *conditional upon the sample outcomes*. To find the (unconditional) expected loss of the whole strategy we merely average these losses (using the marginal probabilities of obtaining the Z_i):

$$0.84(0.42) + 0.1(1.8) + 0.06(0.99) = \$0.6 \text{ million}$$

We note that the "gross" value of the strategy is *identical* (ignoring rounding error) to that obtained under the first option. Thus, the nephew's service yields *no* additional information, and a cost of $10,000 (or even $1) would not be justified.

Evaluation of the third option is still required, however. Since the information is "perfect," we can tell without error which state is valid. For example, if $Y_1 = $ the response that S_1 is true and $Y_2 = $ the response that S_2 is true, the appropriate conditional probabilities are:

$$P(Y_1|S_1) = P(Y_2|S_2) = 1.0$$
$$P(Y_1|S_2) = P(Y_2|S_1) = 0$$

The tree diagram for this option is shown in Figure 2-4. Following through this diagram as we did Figure 2-2, we find that the "gross" expected loss is $0 million (notice that opportunity loss—even with perfect information—cannot go below zero), which is $0.6 million less than the expected loss under prior analysis. Since the cost of the service is $0.5 million, we would take the third option and purchase the "perfect" information; the expected total loss would be $0 + $0.5 = $0.5 million.

In preposterior analysis, then, our objective is to compare *alternative* information-gathering options. In order to do this, we must:

1. List the possible outcomes of each information-gathering option under consideration.
2. Use the appropriate posterior probabilities to find the conditional expected loss of each act under consideration.
3. Apply the marginal probabilities to the expected loss of each "best" act (which is conditional upon the sample outcome) in order to find the "gross" expected loss of the strategy involving information collection and terminal action.
4. Add the cost of information-gathering in order to find the expected *total* loss of each option.

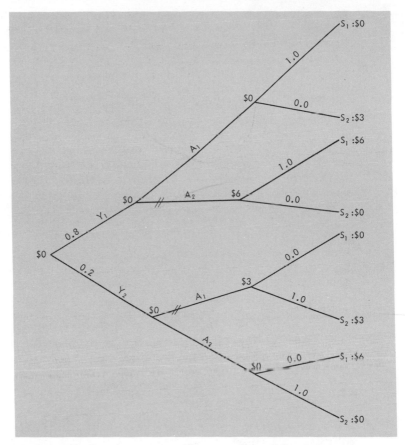

FIG. 2-4 Purchase of "perfect" intelligence service (dollar entries in millions).

5. Choose among options in order to find that alternative which has the *lowest* expected total loss.

As might be surmised, these procedures can be quite complex and time-consuming. Fortunately, some computational shortcuts are available for handling special cases.[7]

Extensions of the Bayesian Approach

The foregoing illustrations, of course, only scratch the surface with regard to Bayesian decision theory. More advanced procedures are available to handle continuous prior and sampling distributions and

---

[7] See Robert Schlaifer, *Probability and Statistics for Business Decisions* (New York: McGraw-Hill Book Company, 1959).

continuous opportunity loss functions.[8] And Bayesian procedures can be extended to deal with sequential sampling and multistage information gathering and choice making as well.[9]

But there are several difficult problems, to which we have alluded earlier, with quantitative methods in general and Bayesian theory in particular: (1) For what period of time should outcomes be computed? (2) What kind of outcome should be considered a relevant measure of effectiveness? (3) How many possible states of nature and courses of action should be considered? Bayesian analysis has been used on long-range planning problems where the "planning horizon" may extend several years into the future. Unfortunately, no fully objective procedures are available for determining just how far into the future one should try to look. In general, the longer the planning horizon, the greater is the uncertainty of the outcomes. On the other hand, the effects of many courses of action extend well into the future; using too short a planning horizon could bias the results. One can, of course, discount future cash flows to present value, thus mitigating the impact of events anticipated over the distant future. Moreover, one can select different horizon lengths and check whether they influence the expected payoffs of the alternatives being considered. These are largely pragmatic devices, however.[10]

Extensions of Bayesian analysis to deal with nonmonetary outcome measures are also possible. For example, monetary outcomes, in principle, can be translated into "utilities" that reflect the decision maker's attitude toward risk.[11] But such procedures are still in an early stage of development, at least in terms of practical applications.

Finally, the problem of determining the appropriate detail in which courses of action and states of nature are to be specified is still largely a matter of the analyst's judgment. Like many quantitative techniques, the Bayesian model becomes computationally complex and time-consuming as details are added.

THE BAYESIAN MODEL AND THE ECONOMICS OF INFORMATION

To us the chief value of the Bayesian model stems from its *conceptual* aspects. It provides a useful framework for viewing marketing research (or other information-gathering activities) in terms of its cost versus its value for *decision* purposes. Virtually all decision making—

[8] See Howard Raiffa and Robert Schlaifer, *Applied Statistical Decision Theory* (Boston, Mass.: Division of Research, Graduate School of Business Administration, Harvard University, 1961).

[9] See Green and Tull, *Research for Marketing Decisions,* pp. 274–83.

[10] For an illustration, see Paul E. Green, "Bayesian Decision Theory in Pricing Strategy," *Journal of Marketing,* XXVII (January 1963), 5–14.

[11] See Alderson and Green, *Planning and Problem Solving in Marketing,* Chapter 5.

marketing or otherwise—takes place under conditions of at least partial ignorance about the variables that will influence the consequences of the decision. Will the new product, now undergoing test marketing, fail or succeed if introduced nationally? Will ad A or ad B pull more reader attention? If we raise the price of our product's economy package by five cents, what will happen to unit sales volume and profits? The illustrations are endless.

Like it or not, the marketing manager is usually forced to gamble and consequently runs the risk of making wrong decisions. The more certain he is of the outcomes, of course, the lower is his risk. Moreover, the better some course of action is over competing options under a wide variety of possible environmental conditions, the less is the cost of being wrong.

Frequently the marketing manager can avail himself of additional information about the consequences of the alternatives being considered. Usually the information will *not* be perfectly reliable and will cost something to collect and analyze. Moreover, the manager frequently has available several information-gathering options of varying cost and reliability. As we illustrated earlier, the questions Bayesian decision theory is designed to answer are basically two:

1. How should the manager choose among alternative information-gathering options, including the option of gathering no additional information at all?
2. Having made this choice, how should a terminal (as opposed to an information-buying) act be chosen with or without the additional information?

Bayesian theory would seem to make it possible for the first time to evaluate marketing research in terms of an *economics-of-information* framework. We believe that the model will exert a significant impact on the design and conduct of marketing research investigations and, indeed, on the organization and administration of the activity itself.

Several implications stem from viewing marketing research as a cost-incurring, information-providing activity. The framework emphasizes the key role *of managerial judgment* in the whole problem-solving process and the relationship of marketing research to managerial action. Indeed, the manager is placed in the position of "make or buy" with regard to information. He can "make" information, using his prior experience, or he can "buy" it through the utilization of marketing research.

This kind of orientation also implies that the marketing researcher must work closely with the user of the information in order to be able to bring his own particular type of expertise to bear on the problem. The marketing researcher's skills can be utilized in a variety of ways within the decision theoretic format. These functions include problem identification, the search for and identification of relevant courses of action, the estimation of alternative consequences of a given course of action and the probabilities associated with it, and the estimation of the reliabilities and costs of alternative investigations.

Finally, the Bayesian approach suggests that data inputs are best assembled through the *interaction of manager and researcher*. Each can contribute his specific type of knowledge and experience to the problem's formulation and solution. Although this may sound commonplace, the truth of the matter is that all too frequently the marketing researcher is not asked —or even permitted—to assist in the structuring of a managerial problem. Rather, he may be directed: "Find out all you can about the market for brand A." If he can implement this type of request, he must serve principally as a "fact finder," unaware of the use to which the findings are to be put, the scale of effort to be devoted to the inquiry, and the reliability required in his findings.

The value of the Bayesian framework, like that of many models, would seem to lie more in the kinds of *questions* it generates than the kinds of *answers* it provides. Although applying the model to actual business problems may require fairly sophisticated procedures, the basic logic agrees with common sense. Its major impact is to force the manager and researcher to look at marketing research in terms of its value in reducing the costs of wrong decisions. If prior uncertainty and the costs of wrong decisions are both low, small-scale investigation or no investigation at all may be indicated. If the potential information is so unreliable that it is inadequate for reducing prior uncertainty, the study may not justify its cost. In other instances, of course, the stakes and uncertainty involved in the decision may justify large expenditures for additional information.

APPLICATIONS OF BAYESIAN THEORY

To date, reported business applications of the Bayesian approach have been sparse. Partly this has been due to the newness of the techniques and partly (we suspect) to reasons of industrial security. However, the Bayesian model has also been used descriptively (as a first approximation) in the development of models of consumer and managerial behavior; we will also discuss some of these applications.

Business Applications

Paul Green has reported three disguised applications in the journal literature [12] and mentioned two others in a book co-authored with Wroe Alderson.[13] Two of these applications dealt with pricing problems and utilized only prior analysis. Another application used prior analysis in the determination of the size and timing of a capacity addition in the

---

[12] "Bayesian Decision Theory in Pricing Strategy," *Journal of Marketing,* XXVII (January 1963), 5–14; "Decision Theory and Chemical Marketing," *Industrial and Engineering Chemistry,* LIV (September 1962), 30–34; "Decisions Involving High Risk," *Advanced Management–Office Executive,* I (October 1962), 18–23.

[13] *Planning and Problem Solving in Marketing.*

face of an uncertain demand for a new product. Two studies dealt explicitly with the evaluation of marketing research expenditures—both in the context of new-product introduction.

Magee has discussed some disguised applications, using the decision tree concept, in capital budgeting and market planning.[14] Hertz has described disguised applications of a related procedure—"risk analysis"— in investment planning.[15] Grayson,[16] Kaufman,[17] and Christensen [18] have discussed various extensions of Bayesian theory in terms of real-world applications, but there is no indication of the extent to which their studies have been implemented. Buzzell and Slater have also presented an exposition of Bayesian analysis in "case" format,[19] but no documentation of the application has appeared. In addition, Newman has presented a case based on partly disguised actual data; [20] he mentions, however, that the managers of the firm did not employ decision theory in the resolution of the problem.

To date, most of the published applications of Bayesian decision theory have been to decisions involving the evaluation of *long-run* changes in corporate marketing strategy. For example, both Magee and Green have reported the use of decision theoretic techniques to help determine whether plant capacity should be increased and, if so, by how much. The time span considered in their illustrations varied from five to ten years.

Because of the focus of these applications on decisions with important long-run consequences, most of the authors report that present value principles were used as a partial basis for determining the flow of cash anticipated from each alternative. In addition, all of the examples implicitly, if not explicitly, have assumed that cash flow and utility are linearly related, an assumption that has been questioned by many.[21]

In spite of the lack of thorough documentation, it seems fair to say that there are some features which differentiate Bayesian decision theory from the more traditional approaches taken in solving long-range market plan-

[14] John F. Magee, "Decision Trees for Decision Making," *Harvard Business Review*, XLII (July–August 1964), 126–38.

[15] D. B. Hertz, "Risk Analysis in Capital Investment," *Harvard Business Review*, XLII (January–February 1964), 95–106.

[16] C. L. Grayson, Jr., *Decisions Under Uncertainty* (Cambridge, Mass.: Harvard Business School Press, 1960).

[17] Gordon M. Kaufman, *Statistical Decision and Related Techniques in Oil and Gas Exploration* (Englewood Cliffs, N. J.: Prentice-Hall, Inc., 1963).

[18] C. Roland Christensen, *Strategic Aspects of Competitive Bidding for Corporate Securities* (Boston: Division of Research, Graduate School of Business Administration, Harvard University, 1965).

[19] Robert D. Buzzell and Charles C. Slater, "Decision Theory and Marketing Management," *Journal of Marketing*, XXVI (July 1962), 7–16.

[20] Joseph W. Newman, "An Application of Decision Theory under the Operating Pressures of Marketing Management," Working Paper No. 69, Graduate School of Business, Stanford University (August 1965).

[21] For example, see Paul E. Green, "Decision Theory and Chemical Marketing," *Industrial and Engineering Chemistry*, LIV (September 1962), 30–34.

ning problems. First, the model provides a mechanism for considering the effects of alternative states of nature on consequences of interest. (Typically, in capital budgeting programs one makes a "best guess" as to the demand that will exist, given a particular decision. This "best guess" is often treated as though it were certain.) Second, the approach is amenable to testing the sensitivity of the outcomes of the evaluation process to departures in the underlying assumptions regarding states of nature, their likelihoods, and the payoff entries themselves. Finally, the approach appears well-suited for coping with the sequential aspects of market planning problems.

Judged from the standpoint of *reported* applications, disguised or otherwise, the use of Bayesian statistics in marketing research valuation (or marketing decision making, generally) currently appears quite limited. Owing to the confidential nature of most corporate studies, this dearth of reported applications is not unusual. (We know of several large companies that are "experimenting" with application of the Bayesian approach.) This is not to say, however, that routine use of Bayesian methods in marketing planning and research is just around the corner. Quite the contrary; we shall see that application of Bayesian statistics to decision making and marketing research evaluation appears to be limited by both technical and computational problems.

Behavioral Applications

While Bayesian theory is essentially normative, it is not surprising that several investigators have evinced some curiosity about its descriptive efficacy—at least as a first approximation—as a model of *human* information acquisition and choice. Others have compared Bayesian outputs with human decision makers' performance in order to see whether a prescriptive model yields substantial economic gains over intuitive procedures.

Marschak has commented on the need to compare human decision behavior with that implied by prescriptive models as a guide for determining both human constraints on the use of normative models and the educational implications for model implementation.[22] Some researchers, dissatisfied with traditional models, have explored the descriptive adequacy of Bayesian models as an explanation of human learning behavior.[23]

Most of the descriptive information-processing experiments have shown a general human tendency to "buy" too much information, relative to that predicted by the Bayesian model, assuming maximization of expected

[22] Jacob J. Marschak, "Actual versus Consistent Decision Behavior," *Behavioral Science*, IX (April 1964), 103–10.

[23] Emir H. Shuford, "Some Bayesian Learning Processes," in *Human Judgments and Optimality*, ed. Maynard W. Shelly and Glenn L. Bryan (New York: John Wiley & Sons, Inc., 1964), pp. 127–52; Violet R. Cane, "Learning and Inference," *Journal of the Royal Statistical Society*, Series A, CXXV, No. 2 (1962), 183–200.

monetary value as a relevant choice criterion.[24] This was the finding even in experiments where information, on one set of trials, was cost-free. At this point it is not clear whether the tendency to overbuy information reflects cognitive limitations or motivational desires to be over-sure. Perhaps both explanations are reasonable in specific situations.

Other more or less general findings of behavioral information processing indicate that subjects can estimate displayed probabilities (relative frequencies) rather well, but have extreme difficulty in manipulating them in Bayesian fashion. Experiments indicate that subjects underestimate high posterior probabilities and overestimate low probabilities.[25] Apparently human beings are rather poor processors of information when compared to the Bayesian model.

The findings of these relatively few experiments suggest that the Bayesian model is not a good "predictor" of human information-processing behavior quantitatively but that it is not bad as a *qualitative* description of the way in which subjects combine new evidence with earlier judgments. Clearly, much more research is needed on situational, perceptual, and personality variables that influence departures from the Bayesian "norm." The fact remains, however, that the model may have some value as a first approximation to the development of *descriptive* choice theory. Departures from the strict rationality of the model might be useful behavioral indicants of personality types and human perceptual limitations.

LIMITATIONS OF BAYESIAN METHODS

Even ignoring the current philosophical controversy between Bayesian and "traditional" statisticians,[26] it is clear that several problems currently exist in the implementation of Bayesian procedures:

1. Bayesian counterparts to many of the traditional sampling and inference techniques are still evolving.

[24] John T. Lanzetta and V. T. Kanareff, "Information Cost, Amount of Payoff, and Level of Aspiration as Determinants of Information Seeking in Decision Making," *Behavioral Science*, VII (October 1962), 459–73; Ward Edwards and L. D. Phillips, "Man as a Transducer for Probabilities in Bayesian Command and Control Systems," in *Human Judgments and Optimality*, ed. Shelly and Bryan, pp. 360–401; Paul E. Green, Michael H. Halbert, and J. Sayer Minas, "An Experiment in Information Buying," *Journal of Advertising Research*, IV (September 1964), 17–23.

[25] Edwards and Phillips, *ibid.;* Paul E. Green, Michael H. Halbert, and Patrick J. Robinson, "An Experiment in Probability Estimation," *Journal of Marketing Research*, II (August 1965), 266–73.

[26] F. J. Anscombe, "Bayesian Statistics," *The American Statistician*, XV (February 1961), 21–24; I. D. J. Bross, "Statistical Dogma: A Challenge," *The American Statistician*, XV (June 1961), 14–15; Allan Birnbaum, "Another View of the Foundations of Statistics," *The American Statistician*, XVI (February 1962), 17–21; H. O. Hartley, "In Dr. Bayes' Consulting Room," *The American Statistician*, XVII (February 1963), 22–24.

2. Bayesian procedures frequently require more computation than their counterpart "traditional" methods.
3. In actual business applications, difficulties are encountered in measuring prior distributions and conditional payoffs.
4. Computational complexities are also introduced in dealing with "many-act, many-state" problems such as sequential decision problems.

Let us deal with these criticisms in turn. As for the first, research that is currently being conducted on such topics as Bayesian regression models, stratified sampling procedures, and the like, is quite promising. For the second, the use of various technical "tricks" allows the analyst to reduce otherwise pragmatically intractable problems to manageable proportions. Still, in many realistic market planning and sample-size-estimation problems, computer routines are almost a necessity. It is interesting to note that reported marketing applications have almost invariably used computer routines in some phase of the computations.

With respect to the latter two criticisms, measurement and computation problems arise as well. If the manager can only express his judgments "vaguely" or, worse yet, if he allows his general optimism (or pessimism) to influence his estimation of probabilities, subsequent computations will be suspect. The analyst may wish to employ sensitivity analysis, in which probabilities or conditional payoffs are deliberately changed in order to ascertain the effect on expected values. Research by Fishburn and others has been addressed to the problem of dealing with cases in which probabilities or outcomes may only be expressed in terms of rank order or according to some bounded interval.[27]

Bayesian analysis is a prescriptive technique for the *consistent* decision maker. Unfortunately, in the real world such ideal decision makers are rarely found. To a large extent, of course, this problem is true of all models, whether or not subjective probability is a part of the framework. It is the idiosyncratic nature of prior probabilities—*as obtained in practice,* not idealized in a model—that worries many analysts desiring to apply Bayesian concepts. While it is true that for fairly "diffuse" prior distributions sample data will tend to swamp initially divergent views (leading to similar posterior distributions), some uneasiness naturally attaches to the use of subjective models.

We share this uneasiness but see no "objective" way out. One can, of course, obtain prior probabilities independently from several executives (who, presumably, have similar knowledge of the problem) and check for interrespondent agreement. One can also conduct sensitivity analyses or utilize some of the approaches described by Fishburn. Still the problem of model validation is ever present.

While we feel that Bayesian methods are less arbitrary than the almost

---

[27] Peter C. Fishburn, *Decision and Value Theory* (New York: John Wiley & Sons, Inc., 1964).

hypnotic use of the "0.05 level of significance," we also believe that serious study of the "predictive expert" constitutes an important research task. Provocative research has already been reported.[28] More research of this fundamental type is sorely needed, not only for the promulgation of Bayesian methods specifically, but for extensions of model-building activity in general.

FUTURE DEVELOPMENTS IN BAYESIAN THEORY AND PRACTICE

Despite the meager list of reported applications at present—and the substantial theoretical problems that will require both mathematical and empirical extenison—we are optimistic about the growing role of Bayesian statistics in marketing research. Various extensions of Bayesian methods, dealing with sample survey methods and customer classification,[29] appear promising for dealing with certain segments of marketing analysis. There is reason to believe that such traditional multivariate techniques as discriminant analysis (see Chapter 4) can be fruitfully viewed within a Bayesian framework. Howard has described a Bayesian-type approach—dubbed "dynamic inference"—as a means for describing certain types of customer brand switching (see Chapter 5).[30] These extensions of the basic model indicate a growing methodological interest on the part of a variety of researchers.

With regard to prescriptive models, we would speculate that Bayesian statistics will be used to an increasing extent in the formulation of multi-stage adaptive models for dealing with such problems as promotional budget determination [31] and capital investment under conditions of uncertainty. Work is also going on in "hybrid" models, incorporating Bayesian concepts with game theoretic models (as described in the beginning section of the chapter). With respect to behavioral research, we would guess that more intensive investigation of the accuracy and reliability of "predictive experts" will be undertaken and that descriptive counterparts of the (normative) Bayesian model will be developed. A normative-

[28] Olaf Helmer and Nicholas Rescher, "On the Epistemology of the Inexact Sciences," *Management Science*, VI (October 1959), 25–52. See also Shelly and Bryan, eds., *Human Judgments and Optimality*.

[29] Rex V. Brown, "The Strategy of Market Research: A Formal Approach," *Journal of Advertising Research*, IV (December 1964), 34–39; C. S. Mayer and Rex V. Brown, "A Search for the Rationale of Non-Probability Sample Designs," in *Marketing and Economic Development*, ed. Peter D. Bennett (Chicago: American Marketing Association, 1966); Paul E. Green, "Bayesian Classification Procedures in Analyzing Customer Characteristics," *Journal of Marketing Research*, I (May 1964), 44–50.

[30] Ronald A. Howard, "Dynamic Inference," *Operations Research*, XIII (September 1965), 712–33.

[31] John D. C. Little, "A Model of Adaptive Control of Promotional Spending," *Operations Research*, XIV (November–December 1966), 1075–97; P. T. Fitz-Roy, "An Adaptive Model of Promotional Expenditure Determination," in *Marketing and Economic Development*, ed. Peter D. Bennett (Chicago: American Marketing Association, 1966), pp. 370–76.

descriptive approach for using Bayesian theory in economic theory has in fact been advanced.[32]

On a somewhat more dramatic level, one could hazard that the Bayesian model will play an important role in the evaluation of marketing research and in its allocation among projects competing for its service. Some industrial firms are already using a framework based on Bayesian concepts for screening potential requests for marketing research (or other information-supplying activities) in terms of value versus cost of its "product."

Perhaps it is not even too much to imagine that Bayesian statistics will occupy a prominent place in the design of future marketing intelligence systems. Already researchers are experimenting with Bayesian models in the processing of probabilistic information for military intelligence systems.[33] Such extensions to commercial systems appear not only feasible but probable in years to come. In this regard it is relevant to note that Bayesian models are already being developed for several types of information retrieval systems.

In summary, we are still sanguine about the future outlook for Bayesian models in research and business applications. We would stress the need, however, for extended study of human judgments as an important phenomenon for scientific investigation. This research is needed, not only for a better understanding of the behavioral implications of Bayesian analysis, but for decision models in general.

[32] William J. Fellner, *Probability and Profit* (Homewood, Ill.: Richard D. Irwin, Inc., 1965).

[33] R. J. Kaplan and J. R. Newman, *A Study in Probabilistic Information Processing*, TM-1150/000/00 (Santa Monica, Calif.: System Development Corporation, April 1963); Edwards and Phillips, in *Human Judgments and Optimality*, ed. Shelly and Bryan.

3

During the last several years experimentation has received increased attention as an approach to evaluating marketing programs. Experimental techniques have been applied to such diverse problems as choosing the best of several direct-mail pieces, measuring the sales impact of different promotional campaigns, evaluating the effect on customer acceptance of varying a product's characteristics, and determining the frequency of salesmen's calls. *Experiments* are defined here as "studies whose implementation involves intervention by the observer beyond that required for measurement." They can be contrasted with *observational* (non-experimental) *studies*, which involve only that degree of intervention required for measurement.

Experimental Studies

Suppose we wanted to determine the effect of different types of packaging on apple sales in supermarkets. We could, for a given week, for each store in a chain, collect a record of the dollar value of apple sales per transaction, together with a record of the different types of packaging that were used during the week. An interstore comparison by type of packaging could then be made to see whether average sales levels differ. Thus far our example has been based on the use of observational data. We could change it to an experiment by requiring all of the store managers to use a particular type of packaging during some specified period of time. We could then measure the effect of packaging on sales by comparing the sales records for the week prior to the intervention with those for the week of the intervention. This form of experimentation is often called a "tryout."

Our tryout leaves us with a rather serious problem of interpretation. To what extent would sales have changed from week to week had there been no special packaging? To get around this difficulty we could divide our stores into two groups, one using special packaging, the other using "traditional" displays. This second group is often called a *control group*. Suppose sales double in the week-to-week comparison in the test group. What are the implications of this change? Is it a valid measure of the effect of packaging?

The answers to these questions depend on what happened to sales in the control group. If they remained unchanged, then the change in the test group is (apparently) competely due to the effect of packaging. Suppose, instead, that both test and control groups changed by the same direction and magnitude. In this case, in spite of the change in the test group, our best estimate of the differential effect of the packaging would be zero.

By specifying what stores are to be included in the experimental and control groups, we can reduce another source of possible error inherent in our observational study. In an observational study, store managers might be free to choose for themselves whether to use special packaging, and a sales increase in stores with special packaging could be attributable to the ability of store managers to discern under what conditions various types of packaging would be effective for their individual stores. If the researcher's problem is to evaluate the use of alternative packaging types, he needs a method for dividing stores into experimental and control groups that will avoid the possible self-selection bias of managers. The principal techniques used for such grouping are randomization and blocking (also sometimes referred to as matching). Their major purpose is to help insure that the different groups in the experiment are comparable before intervention, except for variations that can be ascribable to chance.

The logic underlying the use of control groups, randomization, and blocking (matching) will be discussed in detail in the following sections of this chapter. Suffice it to say for now that experimentation has built into it a number of safeguards against making erroneous inferences about the nature and magnitude of whatever relationship is under investigation. Given the effectiveness of experiments in providing less ambiguous results, one may be tempted to ask: Why bother with observational research?

In spite of the methodological advantages inherent in experimental techniques, observational designs are by far the most frequently used basis for inferring the relationships among a set of variables. Three principal reasons for this fact are as follows: (1) Experiments are often economically infeasible. An experimental study of the effect of grocery-store size on the size of its retail trading area is not likely because the cost of manipulating store size for the purpose of the experiment would be prohibitive. (2) It is often difficult or impossible to intervene in the desired fashion. A study aimed at determining the effect of household income on the likelihood of purchasing a Cadillac could not be experimental because of the impossibility of assigning households experimentally to different income levels. (3) The time required to design and conduct an experiment may exceed the time available before the results are needed. A manufacturer who was designing an experiment to test alternative promotional strategies might have to abandon it before it was implemented if a competitor introduced a new product into the market, because he would have to react to the introduction with changes in his promotional program. At best he might be able to do some survey research to determine customer attitudes toward the new entrant.

There are three types of observational studies: (1) time-series analyses, (2) cross-sectional studies (studies at a point in time), and (3) studies that combine both time-series and point-in-time analysis. Historical time series are usually used as a partial basis for predicting future sales. For example, if one were interested in forecasting annual beer consumption, such variables as disposable income, the proportion of the population between the ages of, say, 18 and 44, and the consumption of competing beverages (wines and distilled spirits) over the past twenty years might be used as a basis for the analysis.

Most consumer surveys would be classified as cross-sectional investigations. They typically involve interviewing a number of customers during a specified period of time, using the same questionnaire. Nothing in the process of interviewing the households is deliberately done to cause them to differ from one another in their responses to the questionnaire. The differences that are observed are presumably due to differences among customers that existed prior to the time of measurement and hence are not a function of the measurement process.

The best-known application of a combined time-series and cross-sectional analysis is the design of a consumer panel, in which the same individuals are interviewed on two or more occasions. The Market Research Corporation of America (MRCA), for example, runs a consumer panel based on a national sample of approximately 7,500 households. Each household fills out a weekly diary of its food and other selected household purchases, and the same households participate week after week. As a result, the data generated describe the historical purchasing behavior of each household. No attempt is made by MRCA to change the purchasing behavior of the participants (for example, by sending them a special 5¢-off coupon for a particular product). For any point in time, then, MRCA has information on each of a large number of households; and the same measurement process can provide time-series analysis as well.

ANALYSIS OF VARIANCE

Analysis of variance is a way of dividing total variation in experimental data into components that can be assigned to specific sources. At first glance the phrase might seem to connote that it is a test of the differences among variances rather than means; but this is not the case.[1] The objective is rather to test the statistical significance of differences among *average responses* caused by controlled variables, after making allowance for influence on responses caused by uncontrolled variables. The label *analysis of variance* is appropriate because if the mean responses of the test objects are different *among* treatments, then the variance among groups will exceed the (independently computed) within-group variance.

[1] For an extended discussion of analysis-of-variance techniques, see Russell L. Ackoff, *The Design of Social Research* (Chicago: The University of Chicago Press, 1953), pp. 229–53.

Suppose we were interested in determining the extent to which the prepackaging of apples in polyethylene bags would increase their sales in supermarkets. In addition, suppose twenty supermarkets had agreed to cooperate in order to perform an experiment. The simplest design we could apply would be a "completely randomized" one in which each of the twenty stores could be assigned to one of two groups in the following fashion. We could draw a two-digit random number from an appropriate table,[2] assigning one to each of the twenty stores. The ten stores with the highest numbers would be assigned to one experimental group and the lower ten to the other group. We could then set up prepackaged apple displays in the first group and bulk apple displays in the second for some specified period of time, say, two weeks. The resulting apple sales in each store could be measured, and at the end of the time period the sales in the two groups could be compared.

The (fixed-effects) model underlying our experiment can be stated more formally as follows:

$$Y_{ij} = \mu + \beta_j + \epsilon_{ij} ; \qquad \sum_{j=1}^{m} \beta_j = 0 ; \qquad \mu(\epsilon_{ij}) = 0 ; \qquad \text{Var}(\epsilon_{ij}) = \sigma_\epsilon^2$$

where

Y_{ij} = sales of the ith store ($i = 1, 2, \ldots, 10$) in the jth treatment (in our experiment $j = 1$ or 2)

μ = average apple sales for a two-week period in the sample population

β_j = fixed effect of the jth treatment on sales

ϵ_{ij} = allowance for experimental error (i.e., the effect of all other factors on apple sales)

Analysis of variance procedures provide a method for estimating μ, β_j, and the variance of ϵ_{ij}.

In the two sections that follow we will illustrate the logic of analysis of variance and discuss the principal assumptions underlying its use as applied to the aforementioned study. Regardless of the complexity of the experiment the fundamental logic involved is the same. Therefore, in subsequent discussion of more complex forms of experimentation we shall not repeat these principles. Those readers interested in a more extensive treatment of both hypothesis testing and estimation procedures should see the references listed in the footnote below.[3]

---

[2] For example, see RAND Corporation, *A Million Random Digits with 100,000 Normal Deviates* (Glencoe, Ill.: The Free Press, 1955).

[3] The following references are listed in ascending order in terms of their mathematical prerequisites: Seymour Banks, *Experimentation in Marketing* (New York: McGraw-Hill Book Company, 1965); W. G. Cochran and Gertrude M. Cox, *Experimental Designs* (New York: John Wiley & Sons, Inc., 1957); Walter Theodore Federer, *Experimental Design: Theory and Application* (New York: The Macmillan Company, 1955); and Oscar Kempthorne, *The Design and Analysis of Experiments* (New York: John Wiley & Sons, Inc., 1952).

The Logic of the Approach

Table 3-1 presents a set of hypothetical results for our apple packaging experiment. In terms of the aforementioned equation, Y_{11} is $45 and Y_{62} is $60. The average sales for the stores in the prepackaged display group $(\overline{Y}_{.1})$ were $57.50, whereas the average sales in the other group $(\overline{Y}_{.2})$ were $37.50. We use the "dot" symbol to indicate the summation over the ith or the jth variable, as the case may be. The information contained in Table 3-1 is plotted in Figure 3-1.

TABLE 3-1   Dollar Sales of Apples over the Two-Week Period (by store)

ith store	Prepackaged display group (1) Y_{i1}	Bulk display group (2) Y_{i2}
1	$45	$70
2	40	5
3	50	30
4	80	35
5	25	40
6	55	60
7	80	25
8	70	50
9	60	40
10	90	20
Total	$575	$375
$\overline{Y}_{.j}$	$57.50	$37.50

Our sample estimate of μ is the grand mean $(\overline{Y}_{..})$ or $47.50. If (as is usually assumed) the expected value of ϵ_{ij} is zero, then the estimated values of $\overline{Y}_{.1}$ and $\overline{Y}_{.2}$ are as follows (b_1 and b_2 are sample estimates of β_1 and β_2):

$$\overline{Y}_{.1} = \overline{Y}_{..} + b_1 \quad \text{and} \quad \overline{Y}_{.2} = \overline{Y}_{..} + b_2$$

or $57.50 = 47.50 + 10.00$, and $37.50 = 47.50 - 10.00$.

Pursuing our logic one step further, we would estimate the difference between average sales resulting from the two treatments as follows:

$$\begin{aligned}
\overline{Y}_{.1} - \overline{Y}_{.2} &= (\overline{Y}_{..} + b_1) - (\overline{Y}_{..} + b_2) \\
&= (47.50 + 10.00) - (47.50 - 10.00) \\
&= \$20.00
\end{aligned}$$

The objective of analysis-of-variance procedures is to test whether the differences among means of two or more populations (e.g., those repre-

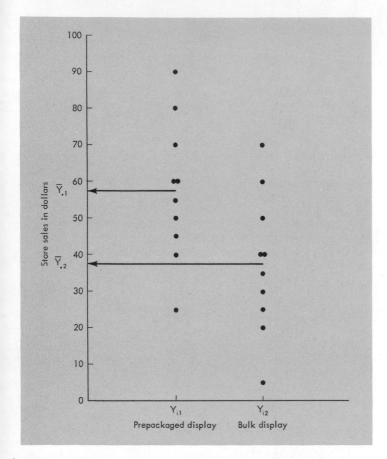

FIG. 3-1 Dollar sales of apples over a two-week period, by store.

sented by the two treatments in our illustration) are equal to some specified value such as zero (i.e., $\beta_i = \beta_j$, where $i \neq j$).

Suppose our null hypothesis is that $\beta_1 = \beta_2$; that is, that the true effects (of which b_1 and b_2 are estimates) of the two treatments are, in fact, equal. Given the results of the experiment as reported above, we can estimate σ_ϵ^2 (the variance of ϵ) in two ways. As we shall show, by comparing the results of these two procedures we can test whether or not the means of the two populations do differ.

First we can *pool* the variances of the two treatments as follows:

$$s_w^2 = \frac{(n_1 - 1) s_1^2 + (n_2 - 1) s_2^2}{n_1 + n_2 - 2}$$

where s_1^2 and s_2^2 are sample variances (adjusted to serve as estimates of σ_ϵ^2) for treatments 1 and 2, respectively, and n_1 and n_2 are the sample sizes of treatments 1 and 2, respectively. Based on our "experimental results," the calculation of s_1^2, s_2^2, and s_w^2 is as follows:

$$s_1^2 = \frac{(45.00 - 57.50)^2 + (40.00 - 57.50)^2 + \cdots + (90.00 - 57.50)^2}{9}$$

$$= \$363.90$$

$$s_2^2 = \frac{(70.00 - 37.50)^2 + (5.00 - 37.50)^2 + \cdots + (20.00 - 37.50)^2}{9}$$

$$= \$368.10$$

$$s_w^2 = \frac{9\,(363.90) + 9\,(368.10)}{10 + 10 - 2}$$

$$= \$366.00$$

The statistic s_w^2 is an estimate of σ_ϵ^2 based on a pooling of the variation from test unit to test unit within each of the treatments.

Another approach to estimating σ_ϵ^2 is to make use of the following relationship, the proof for which is developed in most elementary statistics texts:

$$\sigma_{\overline{Y}}^2 = \frac{\sigma_Y^2}{n}$$

where $\sigma_{\overline{Y}}^2$ is the variance of the distribution of sample means; σ_Y^2 is, in our terminology, σ_ϵ^2; and n is the sample size of one experimental group (assuming they are all equal in size). We can compute an estimate of $\sigma_{\overline{Y}}^2$ directly as follows:

$$s_{\overline{Y}}^2 = \sum_{j=1}^{2} \frac{(\overline{Y}_{\cdot j} - \overline{Y}_{\cdot\cdot})^2}{2 - 1}$$

$$s_{\overline{Y}}^2 = \frac{(57.50 - 47.50)^2 + (37.50 - 47.50)^2}{2 - 1}$$

$$= \$200.00$$

The variance (σ_ϵ^2) can then be estimated by the following formula:

$$s_b^2 = n\,(s_{\overline{Y}}^2)$$
$$= 10\,(200.00) = \$2,000.00$$

Under the null hypothesis, the statistic s_b^2 is an estimate of σ_ϵ^2 based on the variation *between* the means of the treatments that constitute the experiment.

If, in fact, $\beta_1 = \beta_2$, then s_b^2 is an (independently obtained) unbiased estimate of σ_ϵ^2, and its expected value would be equal to that of s_w^2. However, if $\beta_1 \neq \beta_2$, then the expected value of s_b^2 would be greater than that of s_w^2. In the case of our illustration the latter condition appears to exist $(s_b^2 = \$2,000;\ s_w^2 = \$366)$; that is, based on the comparison of s_b^2 and s_w^2, $\beta_1 \neq \beta_2$.[4]

[4] Formal procedures have been developed for testing the statistical significance of the ratio of s_b^2 to s_w^2. Those interested in this topic should see Cochran and Cox, *ibid.*, and Federer, *ibid.* The value of these (analysis of variance) procedures is that they are *not* limited to the two-sample case.

A large part of the "art" of designing useful experiments depends on one's ability to create a design with a suitably high precision (low s_w^2 for the problem under study. Most measurement problems with which marketing management is faced involve test units (individuals, households, cities, market areas) whose "within" variation (given the characteristic to be measured) is relatively large in relationship to one's prior estimate of the likely effect of the experimental variable. This fact leads to the need for somewhat more complex designs than the one just described. Most of this chapter is devoted to a discussion of the principal types of experimental designs that are used to reduce the variance associated with the resulting estimate of the effect of the treatments under study.

Statistical Assumptions Underlying the Analysis-of-Variance Model

Now that we have looked at the computations involved in the single-classification analysis-of-variance model, we can summarize the statistical assumptions made in the model.

1. In the "fixed effects" models which we have assumed in the preceding example, β_j represents the *entire* set of treatments of interest, not just a sample of treatments from some larger group.
2. The error distribution ϵ is normally distributed; $\mu(\epsilon) = 0$, and σ_ϵ^2 is constant over all observations.
3. The effects of treatments are additive.
4. Part of each observation represents an independent "draw" from the error distribution ϵ.

With respect to assumption 1, there are other models (so-called "random effects" models) for dealing with cases where the treatments represent some sample from a universe of treatments.[5] And a "mixed" or composite model is available for dealing with both fixed and random sample interpretations of the group of experimental treatments. Research on the effect of "small" departures from normality and equality of variances (assumption 2) indicates that they do not seriously affect the validity of the tests. Moreover, mathematical transformations (logarithmic, square root, arc sine) are available to achieve equal variance or normality. Transformations are also available to satisfy departures from assumption 3. For example, if the effects of the treatments are multiplicative, the experimenter may use logarithms of the original data.

Departures from the conditions of assumption 4 may seriously distort the appropriate statistical tests. The researcher should attempt to design his experiment to avoid dependency among observations or else use

---

[5] For an appropriate discussion, see George W. Snedecor, *Statistical Methods,* 6th ed. (Ames, Iowa: Iowa State University Press, 1967).

alternative analytical techniques. (Such refinements of the basic model are beyond the scope of this chapter.)

The important consideration to remember is that, aside from the statistical assumptions underlying the analysis of variance, the *variance of the error distribution* will markedly affect the information contained in the results. That is, if this variance is large relative to differences among treatments, then little information may be provided by the experiment as to the true magnitude of the effects.

In the next section of this chapter we discuss some more specialized experimental designs whose objective also is to increase precision.

TYPES OF EXPERIMENTATION

Five types of experimental designs are to be discussed: (1) completely randomized designs, (2) randomized block designs, (3) Latin square designs, (4) double changeover designs, and (5) factorial designs. The first four of these permit the experimenter to manipulate only one experimental variable at a time, while the fifth category, factorial designs, was created for the express purpose of simultaneously experimenting with two or more variables at once. The first four types vary primarily with respect to the extent to which they contain built-in devices aimed at reducing the degree of statistical error that is apt to be associated with the final results. Though our discussion provides a systematic review of the major alternative experimental designs, space does not permit it to be all-inclusive.

Completely Randomized Designs

The simplest design is one in which treatments are allocated among subjects by chance. (The illustration presented in the preceding section was an example of such a design.) The term *treatment* refers to the alternatives whose effects are to be measured—differences in level of advertising expenditure, number of sales calls per customer, or size or type of package design, for example. The most common applications of completely randomized designs are the testing of direct-mail advertising and the evaluation of advertisements using split-run procedures.

The typical procedure followed in conducting these experiments is illustrated by a study conducted by J. William Dunlop on the effect of color of direct-mail advertisements on response to the ads. Renewal notices varying only in color were sent to the members of the Kansas State Alumni Association. Four different colors were used, and every fourth person on the 572-name list received a card of the same color. (This is one standard procedure for allocating subjects to treatments.) The results of the experiment are reported in Table 3-2.

The design of most split-run experiments corresponds closely to that used in Dunlop's study. In the usual split-run test, two different advertisements for the same product are printed in the same issue, on the same

TABLE 3-2   Number of Mailing Pieces Sent Out and
Returned (by color)

Color	Sent	Returned	Per cent returned
White	147	60	40.8
Yellow	144	73	50.7
Blue	141	65	46.1
Cherry	140	54	38.6

Adapted from J. William Dunlop, "The Effect of Color in
Direct Mail Advertising," *Journal of Applied Psychology,*
XXXIV (1950), 281. Reprinted by permission of the American
Psychological Association.

page, but in alternate copies of a magazine or newspaper. The advertisements contain an offer that requires the reader to respond by mail, and the performance of the ads is judged by comparing the response rates to the offer.

Although this form of experimentation has the advantage of being quite simple to interpret, its results in a wide range of research situations are not sufficiently precise to be of much use, because the differences in the response of one treatment and another are apt to be quite small relative to the magnitude of the sampling error. Fortunately procedures have been developed for protecting against the effects of many of these extraneous factors. *Blocking* is one such device.

Randomized Block Designs

One of the common misconceptions about experimental designs is that the test units used must be as nearly homogeneous as possible. Presumably, if the units were completely homogeneous, then any differences obtained after the introduction of the experimental variable would be due to the treatment's effect and not to the influence of some other factor such as store size, degree of competition, etc. Fortunately, complete homogeneity of test units is not a *requirement* for successful experimentation. If one or more of the sources of heterogeneity among test units can be identified, it may then be possible to stratify test units by this variable so that within strata, the test units are relatively *homogeneous,* although there may be a large degree of heterogeneity between strata.

In our apple-packaging experiment, for example, a major source of heterogeneity is store size. Two problems might arise if we were to try to eliminate the heterogeneity by running the experiment with stores of the same size. First, there might not be enough stores of the same size to give us a sufficient base for the experiment. Second, if there were enough stores, how could we be sure that the effect of changing packaging in, say, small stores could be generalized to stores of a different size?

One way around this problem is to use a *randomized block design*. In this type of design, the test units (stores) are stratified before treatments are allocated to them (i.e., the randomization is restricted). In more formal terms, the model for a completely randomized design is revised to include a term representing the effect of blocks on whatever variable (such as sales) is of interest; that is:

$$Y_{ijk} = \mu + \alpha_i + \beta_j + \epsilon_{ijk} ; \qquad \sum \alpha_i = \sum \beta_j = 0 ;$$

$$\mu (\epsilon) = 0 ; \qquad \text{Var} (\epsilon) = \sigma_e^2$$

where (in terms of our apple-sales illustration) Y_{ijk} represents the apple sales of the kth store in the ith block in the jth treatment; α_i is the effect of block i, β_j is the effect of treatment j, and ϵ_{ijk} is the error term, as before.

This type of design has been used by the Schwerin Research Corporation as the basis for comparing the effects of alternative television commercials. Schwerin invites people to a theater to see a program and a commercial. Before watching either, the respondents fill out a questionnaire containing, in part, classification data (e.g., socioeconomic characteristics, brand preferences for certain products) that will be subsequently used as a basis for blocking in the analysis of their responses. After watching the program and the commercial, the respondents fill out questionnaires that record what they remember as well as their brand choices after exposure. In effect, the pre choice factor amounts to *blocking respondents on the basis of their socioeconomic characteristics and/or the brand they preferred prior to exposure.*

Owing to the many sources of variation among test units in the usual criteria of interest to marketing management (sales, market share), there is a need for some type of procedure for restricting randomization; blocking is one such device. Blocking (or stratification), therefore, plays an important role in this and all subsequent designs we shall discuss. By blocking on the basis of a characteristic that is apt to be a major source of variation in the performance (e.g., sales) of test units (e.g., food stores), we can keep the units within each block relatively homogeneous. The greater this homogeneity, the more precise will be the estimate of the effect of the experimental variable under study.

Randomized block designs have been applied also to the study of alternative canned-food display-techniques [6] and of merchandising practices for potatoes.[7] However, in most practical applications, the blocking techniques used are somewhat more complex than those thus far de-

[6] Violet D. Grubbs, Hugh M. Smith, Paul Wischkaempfer, and Nick Havas, *Effectiveness of Selected Canned Food Displays in Supermarkets*, U. S. Dept. of Agriculture Marketing Research Report NA 371 (November 1959).

[7] F. A. Krantz, "An Analysis of Some Factors That Might Influence the Volume of Sales of Small, Medium and Large Potatoes in a Controlled Experiment of Consumer Preferences," *Proceedings of the American Society for Horticultural Science*, LV (1950), 427–34.

scribed. The design that has received the most extensive application to marketing problems is the Latin square, which is described in the following section.

Latin Square Design

In the randomized block design, an attempt is made to increase the degree of homogeneity among test units receiving different treatments by *blocking* on one variable so that all treatments must appear in a given block (usually the same number of times). Latin square designs go one step further than this, in that blocking is based on two variables at once in such a way that each treatment appears once within each stratum of each of the two bases for blocking. The model for the Latin square design is as follows:

$$Y_{ijk} = \mu + \alpha_i + \beta_j + \gamma_k + \epsilon_{ijk} ; \quad \sum \alpha_i = \sum \beta_j = \sum \gamma_k = 0 ;$$
$$\mu (\epsilon) = 0 ; \quad \text{Var} (\epsilon) = \sigma_\epsilon^2$$

where μ is the population mean, α_i is the effect of the ith row, β_j is the effect of the jth column (i.e., the second of the two blocking variables), γ_k is the effect of the kth treatment, and ϵ_{ijk} is the error term.

An illustration of this procedure is reported in Table 3-3 which shows a type of design used by B. A. Domenick to study the effect of various pricing, display, and packaging practices on apple sales in grocery stores.

TABLE 3-3 Schematic Layout of One of Domenick's Experiments

Day of week	Store			
	1	2	3	4
Monday	B	C	D	A
Tuesday	A	B	C	D
Wednesday	D	A	B	C
Thursday	C	D	A	B

Source: B. A. Domenick, *Merchandising McIntosh Apples under Controlled Conditions—Customer Reaction and Effect on Sales* (unpublished Ph.D. dissertation, Cornell University, 1952).

The test unit was a single grocery store. There were four treatments (A, B, C, D), which could be, for example, four different types of apple display. Store and day of week are used as the two *blocking* variables. Treatment A was exposed to store 1 on Tuesday, store 2 on Wednesday, store 3 on Thursday, and store 4 on Monday. Thus, treatment A appeared once in each store and once on each day of the week. This is also true of treatments B, C, and D.

The performance of treatment A (e.g., average sales across the four

A's) can be thought of as a weighted average, where the weights given to each store and day of the week are equal. And the performance of the other treatments is based on the same set of weights for stores and days. The Latin square design therefore insures the comparability of the weights assigned to the experimental variables and thereby increases the precision with which their effects can be measured.

For n treatments the Latin square design requires n rows (e.g., days of the week) and n columns (e.g., stores) and therefore a minimum of n^2 observations. Usually a square is described in terms of the number of rows and columns it contains, such as 3×3, 4×4, or 5×5.

Latin square designs have been applied to a wide range of marketing problems in widely varying circumstances. A number of applications have been focused on the problem of evaluating the effectiveness of advertising and other types of sales promotional tools. In addition to Domenick's work, several experiments have been conducted to evaluate various elements in the promotion of apples. Smith and Frye designed a Latin square experiment to test the effect of color uniformity on apple sales, using the 3×3 design shown in Table 3-4. The rows were three different stores,

TABLE 3-4   Experimental Design and Apple Sales by Treatment
(nine retail food stores, Atlanta, Georgia)

| | \multicolumn{6}{c|}{Experiment period} | | | | | |
| | OcI.–Nov. 11 | | Nov. 13–Nov. 28 | | Nov. 27–Dec. 9 | |
	Treat-ment *	Sales	Treat-ment *	Sales	Treat-ment *	Sales
First replication:						
Store 1	A	779	B	496	C	424
Store 2	B	312	C	314	A	238
Store 3	C	803	A	599	B	314
Second replication:						
Store 4	A	703	C	416	B	319
Store 5	B	376	A	458	C	276
Store 6	C	623	B	397	A	556
Third replication:						
Store 7	A	557	B	382	C	346
Store 8	B	313	C	489	A	396
Store 9	C	170	A	211	B	85

* Treatments represent color ranges of red Delicious apples as follows: A = highly colored (75–100 per cent good red color); B = partly red (50–75 per cent good red color; C = combination (50–100 per cent good red color, i.e., a mixture of treatments A and B).

Source: Hugh M. Smith and R. Frye, *How Color of Red Delicious Apples Affects Their Sales*, U. S. Dept. of Agriculture Market Research Report No. 618 (February 1964).

while columns consisted of three time periods. Three replications of the 3×3 design were included in the experiment, each replicate consisting of a different set of three stores. The results of the experiment indicated that customers most preferred highly colored red apples and least preferred those in the partly red category. As a result, experiments are currently being conducted with electronic sorters to ascertain the feasibility of providing customers with more homogeneously color-graded apples.

Table 3-5 presents another example, one in which 2 × 2 Latin square design was used by a Long Beach, California, newspaper to study the impact of color advertisements on sales of jewelry, furniture, and variety stores. The experiment consists of three 2 × 2 Latin squares run simultaneously. In five out of six of the stores color ads were ahead of black and white on the basis of sales from 45 to 83 per cent, while in one store black-and-white ads outsold color ones.

TABLE 3-5   Experimental Design Used in Studying Impact of Color Advertisements on Sales

Time period	Jewelry stores		Furniture stores		Variety stores	
	Store 1	Store 2	Store 1	Store 2	Store 1	Store 2
1	Color	B&W	Color	B&W	Color	B&W
2	B&W	Color	B&W	Color	B&W	Color

Source: W. S. Hoofnagle, "Experimental Designs in Measuring the Effectiveness of Promotion," *Journal of Marketing Research*, II (May 1965), 157.

Double Changeover Designs

One of the most common devices for increasing the precision of an experiment is to expose each test unit to each treatment during consecutive time periods. This device is illustrated in Table 3-4, in which each of the nine stores included in the experiment was used in three consecutive time periods. In an experiment designed in this fashion the differences in average sales for each treatment will not be due to any systematic differences in store size or characteristics. Thus, one source of potential error has been removed.

But another source of error may have been introduced. If the first treatment (A) administered to store 1 is effective, it may lead customers to stock up on apples and thus result in a lower level of performance for treatment B in the following period. B's performance would be artificially depressed; it would be lower than one might expect if, in fact, it was used outside of the experimental context, because its observed effect in the experiment includes the "negative" *carryover* effect of treatment A, which preceded it.

One can attempt to avoid this problem by lengthening the time period for each treatment or by placing "rest periods" between treatments. But in many situations neither of these methods is feasible. Fortunately it is possible to modify the Latin square in order to overcome this problem.

The "changeover design" permits the calculation of the carryover effects. Table 3-6 presents an example of one such design, using a pair of 3×3 Latin squares.

TABLE 3-6   Changeover Design

Time period	Store					
	1	2	3	4	5	6
1	A	B	C	A	B	C
2	B	C	A	C	A	B
3	C	A	B	B	C	A

Why two Latin squares? Because if only the first one were used, we could not ascertain the carryover effect of, say, treatments A and B on C. C is never immediately preceded in time by A. For estimating the carryover effects on C over two time periods, we have data only for when A is two periods removed. If we are to have data capable of measuring the carryover effect of A and B with respect to C, we need to have measures of the other two conditions, namely, (1) when A immediately precedes C, and (2) when B is two periods removed from C.

Now let us look at the second Latin square. It was deliberately chosen so that it would fulfill both of these needs; store 4 covers the first condition and store 5 covers the second. The same logic can be used for justifying the need for the second square in the case of the carryover effect of A and C on B and of B and C on A.

In an actual application of this design, the American Sheep Producers' Council asked the Economics Research Service of the U. S. Department of Agriculture to help it test its promotional program for retail lamb sales against two alternative programs.[8] The current program (treatment A) used media advertising and merchandising. The two alternatives the Council desired to test were: (treatment B) the use of a cooperative advertising program, and (treatment C) no advertising or promotion of any kind.

Six-week time periods were chosen in order to permit enough time for the Council to promote its regular and cooperative advertising programs and for the retailers to respond to them. Six cities were chosen, three in the Northeast (a relatively high lamb-consuming area) and three in the Midwest (a relatively low lamb-consuming area). In each city a group of self-service stores was chosen at random for auditing lamb and other red-meat sales.

The design was quite useful. It revealed that sales during periods of

[8] Peter L. Henderson, James F. Hind, and Sidney E. Brown, *Promotional Programs for Lamb and Their Effects on Sales*, U. S. Department of Agriculture, Market Research Report No. 522, January 1962.

cooperative advertising were 26 per cent higher than those in which no promotion was done, whereas the Council's regular promotion only resulted in a 10 per cent sales increase over not advertising at all.

An experiment similar in design to the Council's was done for the American Dairy Association to study the effect of varying promotional programs on the sale of milk and other dairy products.[9] A carryover design has also been used to study the effect of different promotional programs on apple sales in supermarkets.[10]

Factorial Designs

Designs that are capable of measuring the effects of more than one variable at a time are called factorial designs. They can perhaps best be explained by an example.

TABLE 3-7   Soft-Drink Factorial Design

Flavor intensity	Sugar content			
	1	2	3	4
1	a	b	c	d
2	e	f	g	h
3	i	j	k	l
4	m	n	o	p

Source: *Product Evaluation: An Examination of Research Procedures* (New York: Market Facts, Inc., March 1962), p. 30. Mimeographed.

A soft-drink manufacturer wanted to find out how varying the flavor intensity and sugar content of his product would affect customer preferences. He set up a factorial design similar to the hypothetical one shown in Table 3-7, for which sixteen different soft-drink formulas were created, consisting of all possible combinations of four different levels of flavor intensity and sugar content. Each formula (a, b, c, etc.) was tried by a different group of people, who rated it on a scale ranging from 0 to 10. The average score of each formula was used as its performance measure.

This example is known as a 4^2 factorial. Two variables, each at four levels, are simultaneously evaluated. The results provide answers to the following questions:

    1. What is the effect of varying flavor intensity on respondent rating for the product?

[9] W. S. Hoofnagle, "Experimental Designs in Measuring the Effectiveness of Promotion," *Journal of Marketing Research*, VII (February 1964), 157.

[10] Peter L. Henderson, James F. Hind, and Sidney E. Brown, "Sales Effects of Two Campaign Themes," *Journal of Advertising Research*, I (December 1961), 2–11.

2. What is the effect of varying sugar content on respondent rating for the product?
3. To what extent does respondent rating on flavor intensity depend on the level of sugar content, and vice versa?

One model that might serve as the basis for analyzing the results of the above experiment is:

$$Y_{ijk} = \mu + \alpha_i + \beta_j + (\alpha\beta)_{ij} + \epsilon_{ijk} ;$$
$$\sum \alpha_i = \sum \beta_j = \sum (\alpha\beta)_{i \cdot} = \sum (\alpha\beta)_{\cdot j} = 0 ;$$
$$\mu(\epsilon) = 0 ; \qquad \text{Var}(\epsilon) = \sigma_\epsilon^2$$

where Y_{ijk} is the score given by the kth individual in response to the test product with the ith flavor and jth level of sugar content, α_i is the effect of the ith flavor and β_j the effect of the jth level of sugar content, $(\alpha\beta)_{ij}$ the interaction of the ith flavor and jth level of sugar content, and ϵ_{ijk} the error term.

When contrasted with the completely randomized design, the factorial design has a number of advantages. In the soft drink example, suppose it was desirable to have a sample size of 640 individuals. This would amount to exposing 40 individuals to each of the 16 product variations. If one wanted to contrast the performance of each of the four treatments for sugar content, one would compare the average score for all individuals exposed to each of the four treatments regardless of the flavor intensity. This amounts to comparing four averages, each of which is based on a sample of the response of 160 individuals. A similar procedure would be followed to compare the performance of different levels of flavor intensity except that the averages would be computed without regard to the level of a sugar content involved. Once more the comparison would be based on a sample size of 160 for each of the four groups.

If a completely randomized design were used to test the effects of these two variables with a sample size of 640, two separate experiments would have to be conducted. Each one would have four treatments, with 160 households exposed to each treatment, for a grand total of 1,280 households. In other words, the factorial design, by testing two variables simultaneously, cuts the sample size required in half (from 1,280 to 640). In addition, the factorial design provides an answer to question 3, above, which the completely randomized design can't do.

Because of these inherent characteristics, the factorial design has been used in a wide variety of situations. Table 3-8 reports the design of a 2^4 factorial diagram used by the Ford Motor Company. The four variables were newspaper, radio, television, and outdoor-billboard coverage, and the two levels of each variable were no use of the medium and relatively great use of it. Each of the 16 combinations of media coverage was exposed in a different geographic area, and actual sales were used as the basis for evaluating the effect of varying expenditures on each medium. Though the company indicated it was pleased with the results, it has not published them.

TABLE 3-8   Sixteen Area Multimedia Experimental Design

	No newspapers				Newspapers			
	No radio		Radio		No radio		Radio	
	No TV	TV	No TV	TV	No TV	TV	No TV	TV
Outdoor	1	2	3	4	5	6	7	8
No outdoor	9	10	11	12	13	14	15	16

Source: George H. Brown, "Measuring the Sales Effectiveness of Alternative Media," *Seventh Annual Conference of the Advertising Research Foundation* (October 1961).

A 2^3 factorial design has been used to measure the effect on chicken sales of varying the kinds of cuts packaged and types of recipe included in the package.[11] In another experiment (a 2^4 factorial) the effect of varying the type and size of packaging on cheddar cheese sales was investigated.[12] Factorial design has also been used to study the effect of varying the level of advertising and the sequence of levels over time on the sales of cookware.[13]

Covariance Analysis

Thus far we have concentrated primarily on experimental designs that directly control or reduce the heterogeneity of the test units exposed to a given treatment by the experimenter. Randomized block, Latin square, and double changeover designs all hold constant some variable (such as time period or store size) that is likely to generate a high level of heterogeneity from one test to another. But it is not always possible to control directly all of the variables that are apt to contribute to the heterogeneity of the test units used in an experiment. For example, one cannot control the number of customers who enter a supermarket or the prices of competing products. And these can be such important factors that if they are not somehow taken into consideration the precision of the experiment can be materially reduced.

Covariance analysis is a statistical procedure for increasing the precision of any of the aforementioned experimental designs. Its value is only beginning to be recognized in the application of experimental procedures to marketing problems. It can be used to remove the *linear* effects of one

[11] Sidney E. Brown, *Increasing Broiler Sales through Offering an Additional Cut and Recipe Materials*, U. S. Dept. of Agriculture Economic Research Report No. 127 (May 1963).

[12] Hugh M. Smith, Wendell E. Clement, and W. S. Hoofnagle, *Merchandising Natural Cheddar Cheese in Retail Food Stores*, U. S. Dept. of Agriculture Market Research Report No. 115 (April 1956).

[13] James Becknell, Jr., and Robert W. McIsaac, "Test Marketing Cookware Coated with Teflon," *Journal of Advertising Research*, V (September 1963), 2–8.

or more uncontrolled variables on the degree of heterogeneity among test units. In the comments that follow we will provide a graphic illustration of the logic underlying this approach. Our illustration will be confined to taking out the effect of only one variable; but the logic can be extended to cases involving more than a single "covariate."

Suppose that a completely randomized design has been chosen for the study of the effect of three different levels of advertising expenditure (T_1, T_2, and T_3) for a perishable food product. Each level of expenditure is exposed in five different cities. In each city ten supermarkets are audited during a two-week period. The sales of the ten stores are averaged, and the resulting figure for each of the fifteen cities is the criterion of performance for the three different levels of advertising expenditure. Suppose at the same time that the average price of the product relative to competing products was also measured in each of the fifteen cities, and suppose, further, that there were no treatment effects. Figure 3-2a presents a hypothetical plot of the sales per transaction (Y) in each of the fifteen cities against the product's price relative to competing products (X). This result would be observed only if X were related to Y and if varying the level of advertising expenditure had no effect on sales.

Now suppose that the three treatments did in fact influence sales. Figure 3-2b pictures such a condition. The average sale per transaction for the three treatments is indicated by M_1, M_2, and M_3. If we fit straight lines through each group of five observations (T_1, T_2, T_3), the lines will describe the average change in per-transaction sales that corresponds to a one-unit change in price within each treatment.

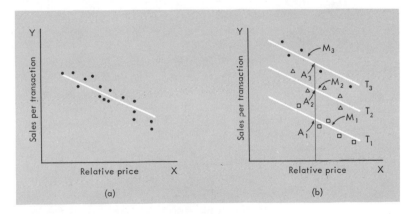

FIG. 3-2   Illustration of covariance analysis.

Taking price into account in this fashion has two effects on the results of our experiment. First, it partially accounts for the difference in the three means (M_1, M_2, M_3). They are different because the three groups of sample cities are not comparable in terms of the average *relative* price for the product under investigation. For example, T_1 has higher relative prices than T_3. This tends to deflate T_1's mean relative to that of T_3. One way to adjust for this situation is to take a given value of X (e.g., its mean across all treatments) and use the expected sales per transaction for each treatment (A_1, A_2, A_3) as the basis for making a comparison of the relative effects of the different treatments. This, in effect, is a device analogous to blocking, except that it attempts to insure the comparability of the treatment by means of a statistical procedure rather than by specifying in advance that each treatment be administered to the same number of low-, medium-, and high-priced markets.

The use of the linear association between Y and X also has the effect of reducing the amount of variation in Y from one test unit to another within each treatment. The degree of precision associated with the experiment without the use of relative price as a covariate would be measured by the amount of deviation of Y for each test unit from its respective mean (M_1, M_2, or M_3). When price is included as a covariate, the relevant measure of precision is the deviation of each Y from its associated linear function (LF_1, LF_2, LF_3). The magnitude of these deviations is less than those from M_1, M_2, M_3. Thus the precision of the experiment is increased by the use of relative price as a covariate.

The addition of covariance analysis to the analytical model of the simple randomized design presented earlier leads to the following model:

$$Y_{ij} = \mu + \beta_i + \gamma \left(P_{ij} - \mu_p \right) + \epsilon_{ij} \,;$$
$$\sum \beta_i = 0 \,; \quad \mu \left(\epsilon \right) = 0 \,; \quad \text{Var} \left(\epsilon \right) = \sigma_\epsilon^2$$

where μ is the mean of the Y population, β_i is the effect of the advertising level in the ith group, P_{ij} is the price of apples in the jth city in the ith treatment, μ_p is the mean price of apples, γ is the change in apple sales associated with a one-unit change in price (as measured about its mean), and ϵ_{ij} is the error term.

This type of analysis can be extended to include more than one covariate at a time. The most important assumption underlying the validity of this approach is that the values of the covariate are in no way influenced by the treatments. For a more detailed discussion of this as well as other assumptions underlying the use of covariance see the works listed below.[14]

Covariance analysis has been used in conjunction with a Latin square design in a study of the effect of various packaging and display conventions on the sale of McIntosh apples.[15] The treatments were blocked on stores and days, and the covariate was the number of customers. On each of four days, in each of four stores, a count of customers was made. (The

[14] Donald R. Cox, *Planning of Experiments* (New York: John Wiley & Sons, Inc., 1958), pp. 48–69; Banks, *Experimentation in Marketing*, pp. 128–34; Federer, *Experimental Design: Theory and Application*, pp. 482–522; and Cochran and Cox, *Experimental Designs*, pp. 82–91.

[15] B. A. Domenick, Jr., *An Illustration of the Use of the Latin Square in Measuring the Effectiveness of Retail Merchandising Practices* (Department of Agricultural Economics, Cornell University, Ithaca, New York, June 1952).

principle involved was the same as that discussed in the preceding illustration.) Use of number of customers as a covariate reduced the degree of experimental error to about 40 per cent of what it would have been had only a 4 × 4 Latin square been used. Those interested in an even more extensive use of covariance analysis should see Henderson, Hind and Brown.[16]

LIMITATIONS OF EXPERIMENTATION [17]

Often experiments are limited to the measurement of short-term response, even though long-term response is more relevant to the problem being studied. In addition, the long-term response of a given treatment is often quite different from the short-term response. If, for example, the advertising expenditures for a certain ethical drug are increased by 50 per cent in an experiment, the effect of the change on sales may not be evident for quite some time. Many patients may have prescriptions that permit automatic refills. Even if doctors are more apt to prescribe the drug as a result of the advertising, only a small proportion of total demand may consist of new prescriptions. Thus the result of the advertising increase would be hardly observable in the short run, whereas in the long run one might find a considerable difference in response.

But the longer an experiment is run, the greater is the chance that something will happen to foul it up. A competitor might introduce a new product, or the sales manager responsible for the test cities might refuse to continue a low level of advertising if he observed that sales were declining as a result. No wonder that the most extensive work in experimentation thus far has been concerned with comparatively simple situations such as direct-mail advertising and grocery-store merchandising of perishable food products.

The expense of accurately measuring sales in individual test units is often relatively great. When retail stores are the unit, measuring is easier, but it may nonetheless involve special store audits. Worse yet is the situation in which sales territories are the experimental unit, for a manufacturer often has shipment data but not retail sales data by territory. One of the most expensive measurement situations occurs when families are the experimental unit. Acquiring valid measures of sales may require either repeated interviews or the use of some type of diary. Not only are these procedures expensive, but they also run the risk of conditioning the respondent by the very process used to measure the response.

The variability of sales from one test unit to another is often quite great by comparison with the probable response to the factor being experimentally manipulated. The amount of fluctuation from test unit to test

---

[16] "Sales Effects of Two Campaign Themes," pp. 6–9.

[17] This section is largely paraphrased from an unpublished paper by John Howard and Harry Roberts, "Experimentation in Marketing: An Appraisal" (mimeographed, about 1960).

unit, regardless of the product involved or the type of test unit (household, city, store, etc.), is often surprisingly large. The greater the degree of this uncontrolled variation, the less valuable will be the results generated from a given experiment. The existence and magnitude of uncontrolled variation in test-unit sales intensifies the need for: (1) rigorous analysis of the extent of this variation as part of the procedure involved in the design of an experiment, and (2) the use of covariance analysis as a variance-reduction technique.

Often contamination is difficult to prevent. For example, it would be quite difficult to prevent experimental group members in a sales-training experiment from talking to members of the control group or to other test groups. Similarly, stores often have overlapping trading areas, and cities have overlapping television-station coverage.

It is quite difficult to run experiments for long periods of time when they require people in an organization to change their usual behavior. In one reported experiment, in which the amount of shelf space devoted to a grocery product was to be manipulated, store managers were found to be quite adept at discovering ways to avoid or delay making the necessary changes. In many of the supermarket experiments, "enumerators" have been used to check each test unit in order to be sure that the instructions necessary for the conduct of the experiment are, in fact, being carried out.

In addition, if people are the test unit and they are aware that they are participating in an experiment, they may change their behavior. For example, sales trainees who are members of an experimental group may improve their productivity because they feel privileged at being included in the experiment or because they are more aware that their performance is being observed, not because of the effect of the particular training program. Fortunately, though people are often the test units in an experiment, they need not be told this in order for the experiment to be conducted.

Frequently one cannot make an experiment sufficiently realistic to be useful. Suppose a product's advertising budget is primarily devoted to national media with neither regional editions nor provisions for split runs. An experiment aimed at evaluating the effect of changing total advertising expenditures would have to make use of media that normally would not be used to promote the product. In addition, competitors often do not respond to tests in the same way that they would if the actions taken were part of the company's general policy.

More serious security problems are associated with experiments than with other forms of research. A field experiment by definition reveals the alternatives that management is interested in evaluating. On some occasions a competitor spots a new product in test market and markets a similar one himself before the testing firm gets its own product on the market.

Often the mortality of test units is relatively high. During the course of an experiment sales territories may change, a salesman may be fired, a store may burn down, or a consumer may move.

In spite of these limitations, the application of experimentation to marketing problems will probably continue to grow during the coming years. A well-designed experiment can usually provide much better safeguards against making unwarranted inferences from a set of results (through intervention, randomization, and blocking) than can nonexperimental studies.

4

Through the appropriate use of intervention, control groups, matching, and randomization, experimental procedures, discussed in the preceding chapter, typically provide a less ambiguous basis for inferring the relationships between a set of variables than do observational (nonexperimental)

Observational Studies

procedures. This is primarily because they do a better job of protecting against errors in interpretation that result from ambiguity as to the direction of causation and from the confounding or co-mingling of effects. By far the more prevalent method of analyzing marketing data, however, is the observational study. This chapter is concerned with techniques for identifying and testing the strength of interrelationships in data obtained by observation.

If an observational study is to provide a basis for assessing the relationship between two or more variables, it must provide a number of safeguards, as nearly equivalent to those provided by experimentation as it can, within the constraints of its budget and the current state of the art in research.

Observational studies cannot provide safeguards as adequate as those given by random assignment of subjects to experimental and control groups, direct manipulation of the experimental variable, and control over some of the extraneous variables that might operate during the course of the experiment. What substitute safeguards are available? For direct manipulation of the experimental variable, the investigator may substitute one or more of several lines of evidence: comparison of people who have been exposed to contrasting experiences, attempts to determine the time order of variables that are associated, examination of the relationship between variables in terms of the pattern of relationships that might be anticipated if one or the other were the causal factor. For assignment of subjects to experimental and control groups, the investigator may substitute evidence which provides a basis for inferring that (or measuring the extent to which) groups of people who have undergone contrasting experiences were or were not similar before those experiences; or he may select from his total group subsamples matched in terms of certain characteristics but with contrasting experiences; or he may restrict his sample to persons with certain characteristics. For direct control over extraneous variables, either past or contemporaneous, he substitutes the gathering of data on other characteristics or experiences of his subjects which he believes may be relevant to position on the dependent variable, and makes use of these data in his analysis.[1]

A number of quantitative techniques have been developed that, when combined with good judgment in the design of the investigation, help to provide the type of safeguards that are provided by intervention, control groups, matching, and randomization in experimental studies. The most important of these are discussed in the pages to follow. They are: (1) cross-classification analysis, (2) regression and correlation analysis, (3) multiple discriminant analysis, and (4) factor analysis.

CROSS-CLASSIFICATION

The simplest and most flexible nonexperimental technique for describing the degree of association between a set of variables is cross-classification analysis. Compared to the other techniques that are discussed in this chapter, cross-classification procedures require the researcher to make relatively few assumptions, prior to the analysis, as to the nature of the relationships being studied. For example, all of the multivariate techniques to be discussed later assume that there is a linear relationship between the variables under investigation (given the way in which they are defined). Cross-classification procedures do not require such an assumption. Several other assumptions that underlie various statistical procedures will be discussed at appropriate points in this chapter.

We can now illustrate the logic of cross-classification procedures. Table 4-1 reports the proportion of regular candy eaters found in a national survey. A one-dimensional table such as this is often of limited value. For although marketing management may be interested in knowing the proportion of regular consumers of its product in the population, it is more likely to want to know why some people consume more than others. Rather than asking "What is the proportion of our customers who consume our product regularly?" it is likely to ask "Are our regular customers systematically different from the general population in terms of income, age, occupation, personality, or media exposure? What is the relationship between the price we charge for our product and the number of people who will purchase it?"

Finding answers to questions such as these requires not only that one look at the consumption of the product in question, but also that he cross-classify it according to whatever variable is of interest. For example,

[1] Claire Selltiz, Marie Jahoda, Morton Deutsch, and Stewart Cook, *Research Methods in Social Relations* (New York: Henry Holt and Company, Inc., 1960), pp. 127–28.

TABLE 4-1   Percentage of Candy Eaters Who
            Eat It Regularly

Regular consumers	67
Irregular consumers	33
Total	100
(Number of cases)	(3,009)

From p. 198 of *Say It with Figures*, rev. 4th ed., by Hans Zeisel.
Copyright © 1957 by Harper & Brothers. Reprinted by permission of Harper & Row, Publishers.

TABLE 4-2   Percentage of Candy Eaters Who Eat It
            Regularly, by Marital Status

	Single	Married
Regular consumers	75	63
Irregular consumers	25	37
Total	100	100
(Number of cases)	(999)	(2,010)

From p. 198 of *Say It with Figures*, rev. 4th ed., by Hans Zeisel.
Copyright © 1957 by Harper & Brothers. Reprinted by permission of Harper & Row, Publishers.

suppose we hypothesize that candy consumption is lower for married than for single customers. The relationship between consumption of candy and marital status is reported in Table 4-2.

The data in the table show that single people do indeed eat candy more regularly than do those who are married. But how confident can we be, based on these results, that marital status is, in fact, associated with candy consumption? For this to be true, we would have to assume that other factors that might also differ between these two groups *are unrelated to candy consumption.* The validity of this assumption in this case is quite doubtful. For example, it is reasonable to assume (1) that married customers are older than single ones, and (2) that older customers consume candy less regularly than do younger ones. If these assumptions are correct, then part of the differences that appear to be due to marital status may, in fact, be a function of age.

How can we determine whether this is so? One alternative would be to construct a table similar to 4-2 for age and candy consumption; another would be to extend 4-2 to include age. We are faced with a choice of looking *successively* at the association of candy consumption with a number of possible characteristics, or, alternatively, of analyzing the full set of variables *simultaneously*.

Successive versus Simultaneous Cross-Classification Procedures

Table 4-3 reports the relationship between age and candy consumption, while Table 4-4 reports the association between age, marital status, and candy consumption. Based on Table 4-3 it appears that age is also associated with the degree of candy consumption. But given our as-

TABLE 4-3   Percentage of Candy Eaters Who Eat It Regularly, by Age

	Up to 25 years	25 years and over
Regular consumers	80	58
Irregular consumers	20	42
Total	100	100
(Number of cases)	(1,302)	(1,707)

From p. 198 of *Say It with Figures*, rev. 4th ed., by Hans Zeisel. Copyright © 1957 by Harper & Brothers. Reprinted by permission of Harper & Row, Publishers.

TABLE 4-4   Percentage of Candy Eaters Who Eat It Regularly, by Age and Marital Status

	Married		Single	
	Up to 25 years	25 years and over	Up to 25 years	25 years and over
Regular consumers	81	58	79	60
Irregular consumers	19	42	21	40
Total	100	100	100	100
(Number of cases)	(503)	(1,507)	(799)	(200)

From p. 199 of *Say It with Figures*, rev. 4th ed., by Hans Zeisel. Copyright © 1957 by Harper & Brothers. Reprinted by permission of Harper & Row, Publishers.

sumption that age is associated with marital status and, further, that marital status is related to candy consumption, we are faced with the same problem in interpreting Table 4-3 that we had when we tried to interpret Table 4-2. What part of the differences in candy consumption is due to age and what part is due to marital status? Neither Table 4-2 nor Table 4-3, either separately or together, provides us with an answer.

Now let's look at Table 4-4. At last we are able to come closer to unraveling the effects of age and marital status on candy consumption. If one holds marital status constant, older customers consume less candy. This is true for both married and single customers, and it confirms the results shown in Table 4-3. However, the simultaneous analysis reveals that candy consumption is not related to marital status, if one holds age constant. The proportion of regular candy customers is virtually the same for married and single customers, whether under 25 or 25 and over. This result contradicts the one that was presented in Table 4-2.

When using cross-classification analysis, if one suspects that one of his assumptions is not valid, he should analyze the variables simultaneously (Table 4-4) *rather than successively* (Tables 4-2 and 4-3). Unless one knows a great deal about the problem under study, successive analysis of variables provides virtually no clue as to what one might expect if simultaneous analysis were conducted. It is perfectly consistent for successive procedures to show a positive association between two variables and for simultaneous analysis to result in either a positive, a negative, or a zero degree of association between them when the effects of other variables are held constant (or, to be more precise, at certain specified levels). The same is also true if one finds a negative or a zero degree of association between two variables using successive procedures.[2]

Limitations

The three most important limitations of cross-classification analysis are its sample-size requirements, its complexity, and the difficulty of being sure that the effects of all other factors have been taken into account. Suppose one is interested in examining the effects on candy consumption of four different variables, each classified into three categories. A table that would permit simultaneous analysis of all five variables (candy consumption plus the four predictors) would consist of 3^5 or 243 cells. One would need a large sample size to get sufficient information as to the proportion of customers falling into each cell. If one were to assume (an unlikely case) that observations would be equally likely in each cell, simply having three observations fall into each would require 729 interviews. For most purposes three observations is not a very large number.

Even if one has a sufficiently large sample size, the interpretation of the results can go from a challenge to a near impossibility as one attempts to work with larger and larger numbers of variables. Suppose one wanted to know about the effect of one of the four variables mentioned in the preceding paragraph, while holding the others constant. There would be 27 logical combinations of each of the other three variables. In each of these 27 cases one could look at the relationship between candy consumption and the fourth variable. Visual inspection of 27 relationships can, at best, be tricky.

[2] For a more detailed discussion of this point, see Hans Zeisel, *Say It with Figures* (New York: Harper and Row, Publishers, 1957), Chapters 8 and 9.

If one is willing to make assumptions such as that of linearity mentioned earlier, then multivariate techniques such as regression or discriminant analysis can be used to help take into account the inter-correlations in the data. This approach will be discussed in the next section. There is an in-between ground, however. One can reduce the complexity of simultaneous analysis by using a procedure referred to as "balancing."

Suppose we want to measure the effect of marital status as it is presented in Table 4-3, but would like to adjust for the differences in the age of married and single customers. There is a much higher percentage of older customers in the married than in the single group ($1,507/[1,507 + 503] = 0.75$, as opposed to $200/[200 + 799] = 0.20$). The proportion of married regular customers reported in Table 4-2 can be thought of as a weighted average of the proportions of younger and older customers, or

$$63 = .25 \ (81) + .75 \ (58)$$

where .25 and .75 are the proportion of married customers who are below and above 25 years of age, respectively. Similarly, the proportion of single customers who regularly consume candy can be also thought of as being generated by a weighted average:

$$75 = .80 \ (79) + .20 \ (60)$$

An attempt can be made to remove the confounding effect of age by using the *same weights* to compute both averages. In this case one might use the over-all proportion of young and old customers to compute the averages (these would be $1,302/3,009$ and $1,707/3,009$). The resulting Table 4-5 provides a measure of the effect of marital status, while "adjusting" for the possible confounding effects of age.

TABLE 4-5   Percentage of Candy Eaters Who Eat It
Regularly, by Marital Status Balanced
for Differences in Age

	Single	Married
Regular consumers	68	68
Irregular consumers	32	32
Total	100	100

Balancing does, however, implicitly build in one additional assumption, namely, that *the effect of marriage on candy consumption is the same for both younger and older customers* (i.e., that the effects of the variable being "balanced for" do not interact with those of the one under study).

Regardless of how well one plans an analysis, there is never any way to be completely sure that the final set of results has not left out some variable which, if it were included, would have an important effect on the results thus far obtained. This problem does not differentiate cross-classification analysis from other observational techniques, but it may be more serious with cross-classification analysis because of the relatively few variables that one can analyze simultaneously by this procedure.

CORRELATION AND REGRESSION

Correlation and regression are techniques for making statements as to the degree of linear association between a criterion (dependent) and one or more predictor (independent) variables. Regression can be differentiated from correlation in that the former assumes fixed values for the independent variables while the latter assumes that both the dependent and independent variables are random. The logical structure of correlation and regression procedures is sufficiently general to make them useful as the principal vehicles for analyzing a wide range of different questions, such as:

1. What is the relationship between a household's socioeconomic characteristics and the quantity of a given product it is apt to purchase in a year?
2. To what extent is the proportion of purchases devoted to private brands by a household associated with the psychological characteristics of the husband and wife?
3. On the average will a 10 per cent cut in the price of a given brand have a greater impact on its market share than increasing retail advertising by 10 per cent?
4. How useful are such general economic measures as gross national product, per cent of unemployment, etc., as a basis for forecasting the sales of a particular industry?

Although the specific variables in these four questions differ, the nature of the analytical problem (finding some measure of either the predictive ability of a set of variables or of the strength of association) is the same. One other characteristic they have in common is that the criterion variable in each of the four situations—e.g., quantity purchased, market share—is measured.

Regression and correlation analyses are appropriate in cases where the criterion variable is measured, whereas discriminant analysis is appropriate for situations in which it is categorical. For example, if one wanted to predict which of several brands of cars a household would purchase, whether a household would own a particular oil company's credit card, or whether the adopters of a new product would be in some fashion systematically different from those who would never try it, then discriminant analysis would be more appropriate than regression.

Nature of the Problem

In most problems of interest to marketing management the criterion variable under study is associated not with a single independent variable but rather with a set of independent variables. This situation can be represented by the following equation:

$$Y = a + b_1X_1 + b_2X_2 + b_3X_3 + \cdots + b_mX_m$$

where Y represents the criterion variable and X_1, X_2, X_3, . . . , X_m are the independent variables. The coefficients b_1, b_2, b_3, . . . , b_m represent measures of the change in the criterion variable (Y) associated with a one-unit change in a particular independent variable, while holding the levels of the other independent variables constant. The constant a defines the value of Y when $X_1 = X_2 = X_3 = \cdots = X_m = 0$.

As an illustration of the application of multiple regression, Frank and Boyd conducted a study of the association betweeen household private brand proneness (PBP: the proportion of a household's purchases of a given product that are of private brands) for regular coffee and fourteen household socioeconomic characteristics, the household's total consumption of the product, and the per cent of total grocery purchases made in each of five grocery chains with relatively large private-branding programs.[3] They started their analysis with measures of each of the aforementioned 21 variables for each of 492 households.

What estimates of a, b_1, b_2, . . . , b_{20} should be used as a basis for forecasting Y (i.e., PBP)? Presumably we would like to choose an estimation procedure that would provide us with as much "information" about the value of Y as possible. One measure of the amount of information a given set of a, b_1, b_2, . . . , b_{20} provides is $1/\sigma_e^2$, where $\sigma_e^2 = \left[\sum_{i=1}^{N} (Y_i - \overset{*}{Y}_i)^2 \right] / (N - k - 1)$. The term Y_i represents the actual PBP for the ith household, and $\overset{*}{Y}_i$ is the predicted PBP, given the actual value of the 20 independent variables for the ith household, together with the set of estimated parameter values. The same set of values is used for all households in the analysis. The letter N stands for the total number of households (492) upon which the analysis is based; and k is the number of independent variables in the equation being used (20).

The smaller the value of σ_e^2, the less is the average squared distance between the actual and forecasted values of Y, and hence the more information is contained in the estimation procedure. Our problem is to find some way of determining what set of a's and b's will minimize σ_e^2, given a particular set of data.

One procedure would be to experiment with a large number of sets of parameter values. For each set of selected coefficients we could plug in the actual values for X_1 through X_{20} for each household and compute a forecasted value of $\overset{*}{Y}_i$. We would then square the difference between the $\overset{*}{Y}_i$ and Y_i, sum the squares for all the households, and divide through by the term in the denominator ($492 - 20 - 1$). This process could be followed, in turn, for each set of parameter values. Ultimately, after con-

[3] Ronald E. Frank and Harper W. Boyd, Jr., "Are Private-Brand-Prone Grocery Product Customers Really Different?" *Journal of Advertising Research*, V (December 1965), 27–35. © 1965 by Advertising Research Foundation, Inc.

siderable searching, we would choose that set of constants which provided the most information (that is, "minimized" σ_ϵ^2). Fortunately, there is no need to go through this laborious (and nonoptimal) procedure, for the problem has been solved mathematically. All one needs to do is solve a system of simultaneous equations for a and $b_1, b_2, \ldots, b_{20}$.

This approach can be generalized to situations in which there are any number of independent variables. From our standpoint, the important thing is not how one solves the equations, but what information the resulting analysis provides as to the nature of the interrelationships and what assumptions are inherent in the procedure.[4]

Four measures that contain most of the information provided by a multiple correlation or regression analysis will be discussed in the following paragraphs. They are the:

1. Simple correlation coefficient (r_{yx})
2. Multiple correlation coefficient (R)
3. Partial correlation coefficient ($r_{yx_i, x_1, x_2, \ldots, x_j, \ldots, x_m}$, *where* $x_i \neq x_j$)
4. Regression coefficient (b_i)

Simple Correlation Coefficient

The simple correlation coefficient is a measure of the extent to which variation in one of *two* variables is *linearly* associated with variation in the other. It has a range of $-1 \leq r_{yx} \leq +1$. Figure 4-1 presents several scatter diagrams representing varying degrees of association between a pair of variables. Figure 4-1a presents three sets of data, each of which has the same degree of correlation ($r_{yx} = 1.0$). Note that the degree of correlation does not depend on where the line falls along the Y or the X axis. It depends only on the extent to which variation in X is linearly associated with variation in Y. (The sign of r_{yx}, however, will depend upon the direction of slope—positive or negative.) In the three plots of 4-1a an above-average value of X is associated with a correspondingly above-average value of Y; in 4-1b an above-average value of X is associated with a below-average value of Y. Figure 4-1c demonstrates that r_{yx} is a measure of *linear* correlation. Clearly there is a systematic relationship between X and Y; but because it is *nonlinear*, our measure of linear association (r_{yx}) is not sensitive to it. Figures 4-1d and e illustrate various degrees of simple correlation.

A standard output of most correlation analyses is a table (usually called a correlation matrix) that reports the simple correlation between *every* pair of variables included in the analysis. In the Frank–Boyd PBP study, the table would have 21 rows and 21 columns, and would contain 441 simple correlation coefficients. Twenty-one of these (the diagonal elements—the simple correlation of each variable with itself) would be

---

[4] Those interested in a more technical discussion of the procedure should see Mordecai Ezekiel and Karl A. Fox, *Methods of Correlation and Regression Analysis* (New York: John Wiley & Sons, Inc., 1959).

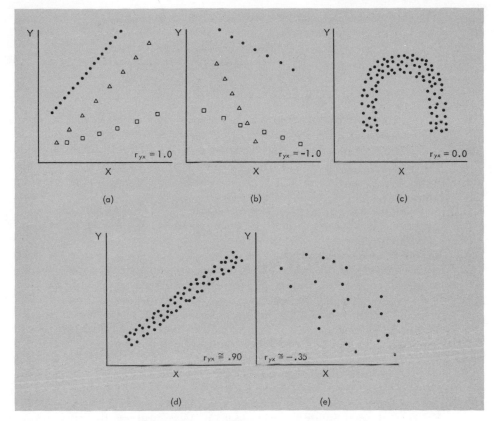

FIG. 4-1 Scatter diagram and correlation coefficients.

1.0. Two hundred ten, or half of the remaining 420 r's, would be duplicates (i.e., $r_{yx} = r_{xy}$). Thus, even for a problem with only 21 variables there would be 210 non-unitary simple correlation coefficients. Table 4-6 reports a small subset of these coefficients for the private-brand analysis of regular coffee mentioned above.

TABLE 4-6   Section of Simple Correlation Matrix: Regular Coffee
Private-Branding Study

	1	2	3	4	5
(1) Number of persons in family	1.00	.37	—.47	.18	—.22
(2) Number of adults in family	.37	1.00	—.00	.10	—.13
(3) Age of female head	—.47	—.00	1.00	—.10	.20
(4) Age of youngest child	.18	.10	—.10	1.00	.03
(5) Housewife employment	—.22	—.13	.20	.03	1.00

The formula for calculating r_{yx} is:

$$r_{yx} = \frac{\sum\limits_{i=1}^{N} (X_i - \overline{X})(Y_i - \overline{Y})}{\sqrt{\left[\sum\limits_{i=1}^{N}(X_i - \overline{X})^2\right]\left[\sum\limits_{i=1}^{N}(Y_i - \overline{Y})^2\right]}}$$

X_i is the ith value of X; in our example of PBP it might be the age of the housewife in the ith household. Correspondingly, Y_i is the ith value of Y. The definition of Y is arbitrary; we could define it, for example, as the degree of PBP for the ith household or as the income of the ith household. The terms $\overline{X}$ and $\overline{Y}$ are the arithmetic means for the two variables.

Though r_{yx} is a useful statistic, its square, r_{yx}^2—the coefficient of determination—is, in fact, a more relevant measure of the degree of linear association between a pair of variables. The quantity r_{yx} is a direct measure of the proportion of variance in one variable, say Y, that is associated with variation in the other (X). Failure to recognize this fact can lead to misinterpreting the degree of association between any pair of variables. For example, an r_{yx} of .5 *does not* mean that half of the variation in Y is accounted for by X. Only .25 of the variation in Y is associated with variation in X. (This same distinction is true of both the multiple and partial correlation coefficients, which are defined in the following paragraphs.)

Multiple Correlation Coefficient

The square of the multiple correlation coefficient (R)—that is, the coefficient of multiple determination R^2—represents the proportion of variation in the dependent variable that is accounted for by the net linear association of all of the independent variables included in the analysis. It thus is similar to the square of the simple correlation coefficient, except that the latter can deal with only one independent variable. The two coefficients differ in that the simple correlation coefficient is symmetrical (i.e., the simple correlation of X and Y is the same as Y and X), whereas the multiple correlation is asymmetrical—it has no meaning if the direction of association of interest is reversed.

The multiple R^2 in the Frank–Boyd regular coffee study was 0.21. In other words, 21 per cent of the variation in PBP was linearly associated with the 20 aforementioned independent variables. The square of R ranges from 0.0 (no association) to 1.0 (perfect association).

Partial Correlation Coefficient

In addition to knowing the net association between the whole set of independent variables and a dependent variable, it is often useful to know the relationship between a particular independent variable and the dependent variable, while holding the other independent variables constant. This is logically analogous to holding marital status constant while looking at the effect of age on candy consumption (see Table 4-4). In terms of the PBP study, it would amount to determining which variables are important contributors to the multiple R^2 for regular coffee. Does where a housewife shops have more effect on her PBP than, say, specific socioeconomic variables, if other variables are held constant?

The partial correlation coefficient for a given independent variable measures the correlation between it and the dependent variable while eliminating any (linear) tendency for the remaining independent variables to obscure the relationship. Table 4-7 presents the partial correlation coefficient for each of the 20 variables in the PBP regular coffee study. The importance of where a housewife shops as a determinant of her degree of PBP is clearly shown. For example, the partial correlation coefficient for the proportion of coffee purchased in the A&P is .39. In other words, approximately 15.2 per cent ($.39^2 \times 100$) of the variance in household PBP purchasing can be accounted for by the variation in the extent to which a housewife shops in the A&P, after taking out the effect of other variables included in the equation. The lowest partial correlation coefficient for a store variable is higher than the highest coefficient for any one of the socioeconomic variables.

TABLE 4-7   Partial Correlation Coefficients: Regular Coffee
Private-Branding Study

Variable description	Partial correlation coefficients
Number of persons in family	.02
Number of adults in family	—.03
Age of female head	.08
Age of youngest child	—.04
Housewife employment	.05
Income	—.07
Occupation	.05
Education	.10
Number of cars	.08
Number of TV sets	.05
Religion of household head	—.09
Race of household head	.00
Building size	—.03
Housewife status	— .01
Proportion of purchases in A&P	.39
Proportion of purchases in National	.25
Proportion of purchases in Jewel	.32
Proportion of purchases in Kroger	.15
Proportion of purchases in Hillman's	.11
Amount of coffee purchased	.07

Note that a partial correlation is not the same as a simple correlation (just as the relationships portrayed in Tables 4-2 and 4-3 are not the same as those reported in Table 4-4). Simple correlation coefficients are measures of association between two variables associated with *successive* analytical procedures, while partial correlation coefficients are measures of association between two variables while taking into account the effects of other variables in the equation; as such they are the result of *simultaneous* procedures.

Regression Coefficient

The regression coefficient, computed for each variable included in an analysis, measures the change in the dependent variable that is linearly associated with a change in the independent variable. Unlike the three preceding measures of association, b is expressed in terms of the units in which the original variables are defined. For example, if the independent variable were income coded in thousands of dollars, then a coefficient of .8 would mean that for every $1,000 increase in income the dependent variable would increase by .8. Increasing the income scale by a factor of 10 would have the effect of decreasing the coefficient by the same factor.

Because of this characteristic, regression coefficients for different variables in an equation cannot be compared without modification. But they are often significant in and of themselves, since they provide information on the expected change in the dependent variable, given a specified change in an independent variable. Thus, one might have some basis for predicting what difference, if any, in the level of PBP one would find between a household with a $5,000 income and one with an income of $20,000. This information cannot be inferred from any of the correlation coefficients.

The magnitude of the regression coefficient associated with a given variable may well depend on whether the variable in question is the only independent variable in the analysis. This is true whenever other variables that are excluded from the equation are correlated with the independent variables that are included. The effect of adding variables which meet these specifications is illustrated in a following section of this chapter, "Inclusion of Relevant Variables."

Regression coefficients can be standardized to facilitate contrasting the relative degree of association among a set of independent variables. For a useful discussion of this procedure see Ezekiel and Fox.[5]

Assumptions

The three most important assumptions made in regression analysis are:

[5] *Methods of Correlation and Regression Analysis.*

1. That the relation between the expected value of the dependent variable ($\overline{Y}$) and an independent variable (X) is linear.
2. That the variation between actual and expected values is the same for all levels of X (i.e., that the error distribution is constant or homoscedastic).
3. That no variable which is apt to affect the dependent variable and is correlated with an independent variable is excluded from the equation. This assumption is not important if one's objective is simply forecasting. It is important if one is interested in the relative degree of association of a set of independent variables with a dependent variable. In subsequent discussion this assumption will be labeled "inclusion of relevant variables."

Linearity. The regression model

$$\hat{Y} = \alpha + \beta_1 X_1 + \beta_2 X_2 + \epsilon$$

embodies the assumptions of additivity and linearity. In the equation, $\hat{Y}$ represents the conditional mean of the dependent variable for a specific set of observations of X_1 and X_2, α is a constant, and β_1 and β_2 are the coefficients that serve as measures of response of $\hat{Y}$ (estimated by $\overset{*}{Y}$) to each of the variables as represented by X_1 and X_2.

Additivity implies that the effect β_1 on $\hat{Y}$ of variable X_1 is independent of the level of the other variable, X_2. Suppose, for example, that $\hat{Y}$ is the market share for brand M at time t, X_1 is an index of brand M's price relative to that of competing brands at time t, and X_2 is an index of the degree of dealing (coupons, cents-off sales, etc.) for brand M relative to that of competitors at t. The equation states that a cut in price will have an effect (β_1) on $\hat{Y}$, the magnitude of which will be the same regardless of the level of dealing (X_2) that is being engaged in by the brand. If, in reality, the effect of a cut in price is related to the degree of dealing or the level of some other promotional variable, then the assumption of additivity is being violated. The importance of the violation depends on the nature and extent of the relationship between the price response and the levels of the other promotional variables, as well as upon the economics of the decision problem to which the analysis is related.

The assumption of linearity embraces the assumption of additivity but goes further, for it assumes that the change in response of $\hat{Y}$ to unit changes in X_1 is the same for all levels of X_1. Or, to put it another way, it assumes that there is a straight-line relationship between $\hat{Y}$ and X_1.

Equality of Variance. If a linear function were fitted to the relationship between Y and X pictured in Figure 4-2a, the amount of variation (as defined by the variance σ_ϵ^2) between the actual and expected values of Y would be the same for all levels of X. In the case of Figure 4-2b or c

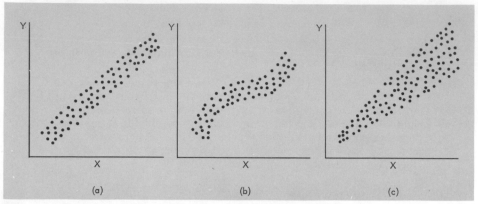

FIG. 4-2   Illustration of heteroscedasticity. Redrawn from Ronald E. Frank, "Use of Transformation," *Journal of Marketing Research*, III (August 1966), 249.

the fitting of a linear function would result in errors between the actual and forecasted value of Y that vary from one level of X to another. In these two cases the assumption of constant variance σ_ϵ^2 is violated, and this violation can increase the uncertainty (or, alternatively, decrease the amount of information) associated with one's estimate of the effect of X on Y.

A further assumption—that the differences between actual and expected share (the ϵ's) are normally distributed—is also important, especially with respect to the validity of the standard procedures for determining confidence limits and conducting statistical tests. Our discussion, however, has not focused on this assumption because one typically has little information on the distribution of ϵ that is not bound up in the questions of linearity and equality of variance. If departures from these latter assumptions can be handled adequately, the chances are reasonably good that departures from normality will not be too serious.

Inclusion of Relevant Variables.   Failure to include a variable that is correlated with both the dependent variable and one or more of the independent variables in the equation can lead to a serious bias in the estimates (b_i) of the magnitude of the regression coefficients (β_i) of the variables that are included in the model. For example, suppose we are interested in the relationship between brand M's market share (Y) in a week (t) and its advertising activity relative to competing brands (X_2), and that we use the following model:

$$\hat{Y} = \alpha + \beta X_2 + \epsilon$$

Figure 4-3 presents a scatter diagram of the weekly values of X_2 and Y for M (ignoring momentarily M's price level). Line A represents a freehand estimate of what this relationship would look like. The slope of this line represents an estimate of the effect of advertising on market share.

If we add to our equation data on M's relative price (X_1) for each week, we get the following model:

$$\hat{Y} = \alpha + \beta_1 X_1 + \beta_2 X_2 + \epsilon$$

Looking at Figure 4-3 we can see that price is correlated with Y and to

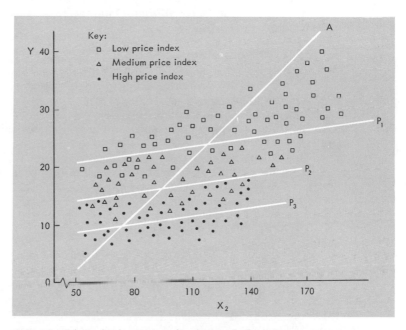

FIG. 4-3   Relationship between market share and advertising.

some extent with X_2; in the first equation we had in effect excluded a relevant variable. The effect of this exclusion can be graphically seen by comparing the slope of A with the three parallel lines P_1, P_2, and P_3. Line P_1 represents the relationship between advertising and market share holding price at a low level, while P_2 and P_3 represent the same relationship for price at medium and high levels, respectively.

A rough estimate of β_2 would be the average of the slopes of P_1, P_2, and P_3. Clearly $b > b_2$. In other words, excluding a relevant variable, price, from our model would result in a substantial overstatement of the true effect (β_2) of advertising on sales.

Fortunately, there are procedures for testing for the degree of linearity and equality of variance in a set of data. And where the data do depart from these assumptions, there are procedures that frequently permit one to get around the problem. Although these are beyond the scope of our discussion, they are included in most texts on the subject. But there are no statistical tests that tell one whether all of the relevant variables have been included in an analysis. The best one can do is attempt to include all of those that he believes to be relevant, based on past research and his own judgment as well as that of others.

Applications

Regression and correlation techniques have been used as the basis for, among other things:

1. Analyzing the relationship between the weekly market share for a brand of a frequently purchased food product and its price, dealing, retailing, and advertising activity, as well as that of its competitors.[6]
2. Forecasting the expected sales of a broad range of nondurable and durable consumer products as well as industrial products—beer, women's clothing, automobiles, machine tools, plywood, and plumbing fixtures.[7]
3. Determining the extent to which the rate of a household's consumption of a specific food product is correlated with its demographic and socioeconomic characteristics.[8]
4. Determining the degree of association between the psychological and socioeconomic characteristics of insurance salesmen and their over-all sales performance.

DISCRIMINANT ANALYSIS

Many marketing decisions depend, in part, on management's assumptions as to what socioeconomic, attitudinal, and other factors distinguish one group of customers from another. For example, in designing the promotional campaign for a particular brand of car one would like to know what characteristics differentiate customers who purchase it from those who purchase, say, each of the three major competing brands in the same price class, or what factors differentiate customers who buy one model from those who buy another. There is similar interest in finding out the differences between light and heavy users, loyal and nonloyal customers, customers who shop in one type of outlet and those who shop in another, etc.

For the marketing model builder the common characteristic of these problems is their focus on determining what factors are associated with the probability of a customer's falling into one of several categories. That is, they are concerned with the prediction of a categorical variable, such as whether a customer will buy brand A, B, or C or shop in store

[6] Ronald E. Frank and William F. Massy, "Market Segmentation and the Effectiveness of a Brand's Price and Dealing Policies," *Journal of Business*, XXXVIII, No. 2 (April 1965), 186–200.

[7] Milton Spencer, Colin Clark, and Peter Hoguet, *Business and Economic Forecasting* (Homewood, Illinois: Richard D. Irwin, Inc., 1961).

[8] Ronald E. Frank, William F. Massy, and Harper W. Boyd, Jr., *Media Selection and Customers in the Heavy Half*. Mimeographed. March 1966.

A or B. Standard multiple regression analysis, except where dealing with only two groups, cannot be adapted to the prediction of other than measured variables such as total consumption or market share. *Discriminant analysis* is the technique that is used for dealing with categorical variables such as the ones mentioned above. For purposes of illustration, we shall deal with discriminant analysis where only two choices are involved; but N-way discriminant analysis (for $N > 2$) is available for dealing with multiple categories.

Logic of the Technique

Assume that an industrial marketing researcher, working for a synthetic fibers firm, wants to find out whether a new industrial yarn his firm is developing will be commercially acceptable. The firm hopes to sell its yarn for fabrication into industrial belting. In carrying out his investigation suppose the researcher is primarily interested in ascertaining the relative importance of the following four yarn characteristics on potential buyers' over-all evaluation of a product's "desirability" for industrial belting: durability; light weight; low investment in conversion facilities; and rot resistance. The researcher might employ discriminant analysis in two ways. One would be to prepare a group of variants of the product and to ask potential buyers to rate each variant for each of the four characteristics and—assuming equal prices—to tell him which variants they would consider buying. Or he could merely show them ratings for each characteristic for each variant and ask them which if any of the variants they would consider for purchase. (The latter would be appropriate if he thought that differences among subjective ratings of the characteristics would be small.) If, in either case, the response "would buy the yarn" was always associated with a high rating for durability and the response "wouldn't buy it" was always associated with a low rating for durability, he could conclude that durability is a characteristic that discriminates well in the separation of buyers from nonbuyers. If he found that about as many people said they would as said they wouldn't buy variants with a high rating for light weight, then "light weight" would be a characteristic that discriminates poorly between buyers and nonbuyers. (In rating the variants, each potential buyer would, of course, be implicitly comparing them with products already on the market.)

For purposes of illustration, we will assume that the ratings in Table 4-8 pertain to only one of the product variants being considered, that they represent the judgments of 12 potential buyers of the product, and that a particular price was stipulated in the survey. (In repetitive surveys one could experimentally vary the price in order to determine its relationship to product characteristics and purchase versus nonpurchase response.) As can be noted from the data in Table 4-8, the mean rating difference between buyer and nonbuyer within the category "durability" is high $(8.29 - 3.20 = 5.09)$, and the amount of durability in the product would be likely to please most of the potential buyers. On the other hand, the

TABLE 4-8 Hypothetical Ratings for Research Product Y (0 = very poor to 10 = excellent)

	Durability	Light weight	Low investment	Rot resistance
"Would buy"				
	9	8	7	6
	7	6	6	5
	10	7	8	2
	8	4	5	4
	9	9	3	3
	8	6	7	2
	7	5	6	2
	—	—	—	—
Mean rating	8.29	6.43	6.00	3.43
"Wouldn't buy"				
	4	4	4	6
	3	6	6	3
	6	3	3	4
	2	4	5	2
	1	2	2	1
	—	—	—	—
Mean rating	3.20	3.80	4.00	3.20

characteristic "light weight" has a difference between mean ratings of only 2.63 (6.43 − 3.80), and we might expect this characteristic to be less discriminating in terms of a buy versus not-buy decision.

The first step in the analysis would be to estimate the coefficients of the following linear discriminant function: [9]

$$D = b_1 X_{1i} + b_2 X_{2i} + b_3 X_{3i} + b_4 X_{4i}$$

where X_{1i} through X_{4i} are the values of the ith buyer for each of four yarn characteristics. D is a new score computed for each buyer by plugging the value of his scores for each of the four characteristics into the above equation and then multiplying by their respective coefficients and summing. A critical value of D is determined as a basis for classifying all individuals into one group or the other. The computation procedures for arriving at the D coefficient insure that the proportion of individuals whose predicted group membership matches their actual membership is maximized.

Figure 4-4 presents a graphic illustration of a hypothetical discriminant analysis. Suppose B represents the buy group, NB the not-buy group, and X_1 and X_2 represent the scores for the first two yarn characteristics. Each

[9] For a discussion of these procedures see William F. Massy, "Discriminant Analysis of Audience Characteristics," *Journal of Advertising Research*, V, No. 1 (March 1965), 39–48.

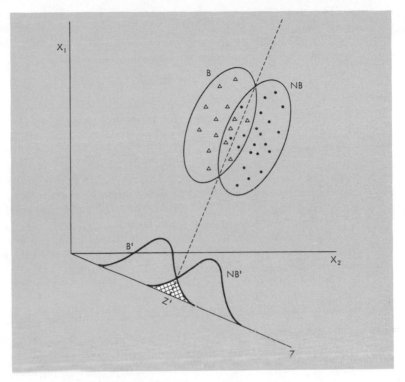

FIG. 4-4 Illustration of a linear discriminant analysis.

item plotted illustrates both the group membership (N or NB, labeled x or o) and the values of a given buyer with respect to characteristics X_1 and X_2.

The resultant ellipses enclose some specified proportion of the points, say 95 per cent. If a straight line is drawn through the two points where the ellipses intersect and then projected to a perpendicular axis Z, we can say that the overlap between the univariate distributions N' and NB' (represented by the shaded area) is smaller than would be obtained by any other line drawn through the ellipses formed by the scatter plots. In dealing with more than two measurements (as described in the illustration) we would, of course, have to increase the dimensionality of the space. In any case, however, our projection would result in two *univariate* distributions representing the linear compounds obtained from the discriminant function.

In each case we can compute a new score Z_i for the ith individual. If Z_i is greater than Z', then the probability that the ith person belongs to the NB group is greater than that he belongs to B. The dashed line is computed to make the use of Z' as the breakpoint maximize the proportion of buyers that will be correctly classified.

The coefficients of the discriminant function are also useful in that they yield information about the relative [10] importance of each product characteristic insofar as discrimination between buy versus not-buy is concerned. For our hypothetical example, this equation turns out to be

$$D = 0.049X_1 + 0.005X_2 + 0.011X_3 - 0.016X_4$$

where X_1, X_2, X_3, and X_4 are, respectively, the scores for durability, light weight, low investment, and rot resistance. Characteristic X_1, durability, is much more important than characteristic X_2, light weight, in terms of discriminating between buyers and nonbuyers (after the interrelationships of all the variables are taken into account). The fact that characteristic X_4, rot resistance, carries a negative sign is not too surprising. First, considered singly, its discriminating power is relatively small ($3.43 - 3.20 = 0.23$). Second, as it turns out, when the interrelationships of X_4 with the other variables are considered, low scores for X_4 happen to be associated with combinations of high scores for the other variables. (In either event it would *not* be a characteristic we would be highly desirous of improving, say, compared to characteristics X_1 and X_3.)

Outside of scientific circles (where it is extensively used in classificatory problems) linear discriminant analysis is still a little-known technique; but its use in multidimensional rating problems with categorical data seems likely to increase. It can be extended to N-group classifications ($N > 2$), and additional considerations such as prior probabilities can be incorporated in it. Various computational techniques are available for computing discriminant functions, and procedures are available for testing the hypothesis that the means of all the variables are the same for all groups. All these considerations are beyond the scope of this introductory discussion; interested readers should consult Massy's article, cited earlier.[11]

Assumptions

In discriminant analysis each of the N populations is assumed to be multivariate normal. The absolute values of the coefficients (the b's) are of no significance. The only meaningful comparison of the b's is their relative magnitude, which serves as a measure of the relative importance of each of the independent variables (X_1, X_2, etc.).

The assumptions for obtaining unbiased estimates of the b's have not been formally worked out for discriminant analysis. However, it is quite likely that the assumptions are similar to those for regression—namely, that excluded variables must be uncorrelated with those independent variables in the equation if the estimates of the b's are to be unbiased.

---

[10] Strictly speaking, the coefficients should be divided by their own standard deviation; however, score variances are roughly equal in this example.
[11] "Discriminant Analysis of Audience Characteristics."

Applications

Discriminant analysis has been applied to a rather diverse set of problems, such as determining:

1. The degree of similarity between the audiences of different FM stations based on audience socioeconomic and attitudinal data.[12]
2. The socioeconomic and purchase characteristics of households that are most apt to adopt a newly introduced brand of an established product category.[13]
3. The extent to which the socioeconomic and personality characteristics of individuals are apt to predict whether they will purchase a Ford or a Chevrolet.[14]
4. The extent to which household socioeconomic and personality characteristics can be used to predict the use of thrift deposits in either commercial banks or savings and loan associations.[15]

FACTOR ANALYSIS

The term *factor analysis* represents a group of techniques that are used to analyze the intercorrelations within a set of variables. Its primary purpose is to find a way of summarizing the information contained in a number of original variables into a smaller set of new variables with a minimum loss of information—that is, to remove the redundancy in the original measurements. The original need for such a technique was first expressed in psychology when attempts were made to describe an individual's personality in terms of his answers to, say, 50 or more sets of tests. The questions facing the researcher in this context were: To what extent can these 50 measures be reduced to a smaller number of dimensions? To what extent do responses to different tests measure the same phenomena?

The four functions that factor analysis can perform are: [16]

[12] *Ibid.*

[13] Ronald E. Frank, William F. Massy, and Donald G. Morrison, "The Determinants of Innovative Behavior with Respect to a Branded Frequently Purchased Food Product," *Proceedings* of the Winter Meeting of the American Marketing Association, New York, December 1964.

[14] Franklin B. Evans, "Psychological and Objective Factors in the Prediction of Brand Choice: Ford versus Chevrolet," *Journal of Business*, XXXII, No. 4 (October 1959), 340–69.

[15] Henry Claycamp, "Characteristics of Thrift Deposit Owners," *Journal of Marketing Research*, II, No. 2 (May 1965), 163–70.

[16] For more detailed discussion of each of the functions, see William F. Massy, "Applying Factor Analysis to a Specific Marketing Problem," in *Toward Scientific Marketing*, ed. Stephen A. Greyser (Chicago: American Marketing Association, 1964), pp. 291–307.

1. Finding a set of dimensions that are latent in a large set of variables. The aforementioned problem of personality measurement is an example of this function.

2. Finding a way to group people into distinctly different groups within a larger population. This approach might be useful for describing the extent and nature of existing market segments (i.e., groups of customers whose buying patterns are similar within a segment but differ widely from segment to segment).

3. Identifying likely variables for subsequent regression or discriminant analysis from a much larger set of variables. For example, in a study of household private-brand proneness for 44 specific grocery products [17] a decision was made to delete age of husband as an independent variable in the analysis because it had an extremely high correlation with the wife's age. That is, the information contained in the two measures was largely redundant, and thus it was necessary to include only one of the two variables in the analysis.

4. Creating an entirely new set of a smaller number of variables to replace either in part or completely the original set of variables for inclusion in subsequent regression or discriminant analysis. In a study of the variation in television ownership in 240 urban areas Massy conducted a factor analysis of 27 variables (the percentage distribution of households in 14 income categories and 9 educational categories as well as 4 measures of television coverage). Of the original 27 variables no more than 10 resulting new measures were utilized in subsequent regression analysis.[18]

From the illustrations listed above it is clear that factor analysis is a complementary, not a competitive, tool relative to cross-classification, regression, or discriminant analysis.

Logic of the Analysis

Several numerical procedures are available for performing factor analyses, but in this chapter we consider only one—*principal components analysis*. Principal components analysis is a factor analytic technique that systematically extracts factors sequentially with the objective of producing maximum discrimination among individuals by determining what the various tests are measuring in common. Variation that is "unexplained" by the first factor may be, in part, explained by a second factor —which is independent of the first—and so on, until it is not worthwhile to extract more factors.

Frequently, the starting point for conducting a factor analysis is the correlation matrix obtained by computing all correlation coefficients for

[17] Frank and Boyd, "Are Private-Brand-Prone Grocery Product Customers Really Different?" *Journal of Advertising Research*, V, No. 4 (December 1965), 27–35.

[18] William F. Massy, "Television Ownership in 1950," in Ronald E. Frank, Alfred A. Kuehn, and William F. Massy, *Quantitative Techniques in Marketing Analysis* (Homewood, Ill.: Richard D. Irwin, Inc., 1962), pp. 440–60.

a set of test variables taken two at a time. The data of Table 4-9 represent such a matrix of correlation coefficients, derived from scores on five per-

TABLE 4-9 Intercorrelation Coefficients—Five Personality Test Scores

Test	1	2	3	4	5
1. Atwell-Wells Vocabulary	1.00	0.22	−0.23	−0.23	0.07
2. Gordon "responsibility"	0.22	1.00	0.18	−0.17	0.07
3. Gough-Sanford Rigidity	−0.23	0.18	1.00	0.24	0.01
4. Rotter Social Reaction	−0.23	−0.17	0.24	1.00	−0.25
5. Gordon "sociability"	0.07	0.07	0.01	−0.25	1.00

sonality tests for a group of thirty-six graduate students. The five tests may be described as follows:

1. The Atwell and Wells Wide Range Vocabulary Test is an indicator of general intelligence level.
2. The Gordon Personal Profile Test attempts to classify subjects on the basis of four personality characteristics: ascendancy, responsibility, emotional stability, and sociability. In our factor analysis we shall use the test results for responsibility and sociability.
3. The Gough-Sanford Rigidity Test attempts to measure the extent of a subject's open-mindedness or closed-mindedness, that is, his degree of attitude rigidity.
4. The Rotter Social Reaction Inventory Test purports to measure the degree of one's "felt control over his environment," that is, the extent to which he feels he can influence events.

Note in Table 4-9 that the correlation coefficients are symmetrical around the main diagonal, 1.00, 1.00, etc., and that they tend to cluster for tests 1 through 4 but that test 5 (with the exception of a correlation of −0.25 with test 4) exhibits little intercorrelation with the other tests. Can we extract from these figures underlying factors that are independent of one another and that account for most of the variability in the original set of data? Suppose, *a priori*, that we wish to extract three independent factors (that is, ones whose intercorrelation is zero) in order to see how much of the total variation can be explained by only three rather than five variables. Table 4-10 summarizes the results obtained by applying principal components analysis.

We note from Table 4-10 that the first factor, Factor I, accounts for 32 per cent of the total variation in the data, and that test 4 appears to be rather heavily loaded on this factor. (*Loading* is the correlation of the test with the factor.) Factor II adds 24 percentage points (56 − 32) and exhibits high loadings on tests 2 and 3. Factor III adds 19 percentage points and is heavily loaded on test 5. All together the three factors

TABLE 4-10   Extraction of Three Factors from Original
Correlation Matrix

Test	Factor loadings		
	I	II	III
1. Atwell-Wells Vocabulary	—0.53	—0.04	—0.48
2. Gordon "responsibility"	—0.31	0.67	—0.37
3. Gough-Sanford Rigidity	0.36	0.70	0.06
4. Rotter Social Reaction	0.60	0.03	—0.21
5. Gordon "sociability"	—0.35	0.24	0.76
Cumulative proportion of variation	32%	56%	75%

account for 75 per cent of the variation in the data. *Interpretation* of
these factors (that is, assigning meaning to them) is a different matter,
however. We might be tempted to say that tests 2 and 3 are some measures of "inner-directedness" and that test 5 appears to be a measure of
"other-directedness." Techniques are available for "factor rotation" to
achieve a more meaningful labeling of the underlying constructs; but all
in all, we are better off leaving the identification of the factors to someone
trained in personality theory. Ideally we would like one or more tests to
be highly loaded with a particular factor and the rest to carry loadings
near zero. Notice that is not the case, particularly with regard to Factor I;
all tests have at least moderate loadings on this factor.

Note, however, that we have succeeded in accounting for about three-
quarters of the original variation in the data in terms of three rather than
five variables. We could proceed to reproduce the original correlation
matrix—with some error, of course—by "matrix multiplication." Illus-
trating this procedure for the first cell entry (1.00) and the second cell
entry (0.22) in Table 4-9, we have:

$$-0.53\,(-0.53) - 0.04\,(-0.04) - 0.48\,(-0.48) = 0.5129$$

$$-0.53\,(-0.31) - 0.04\,(+0.67) - 0.48\,(-0.37) = 0.3151$$

Similarly, we multiply each row by every other row. The results are
shown in Table 4-11. As we can note by comparing Table 4-11 with Table
4-9 we have not reproduced the original intercorrelation perfectly, which
is to be expected since we have lost some information in reducing the
data.

The interpretation of factor analysis can be aided by graphical analysis.
Figure 4-5 plots the loadings for Factor II and III from Table 4-10. Since
principal components analysis produces "orthogonal" or independent

TABLE 4-11 "Reproduced" Intercorrelation Matrix

Test	1	2	3	4	5
1. Atwell-Wells Vocabulary	0.51	0.32	—0.25	—0.22	—0.19
2. Gordon "responsibility"	0.32	0.68	0.34	—0.09	—0.01
3. Gough-Sanford Rigidity	—0.25	0.34	0.62	0.22	0.09
4. Rotter Social Reaction	—0.22	—0.09	0.22	0.41	—0.36
5. Gordon "sociability"	—0.19	—0.01	0.09	—0.36	0.76

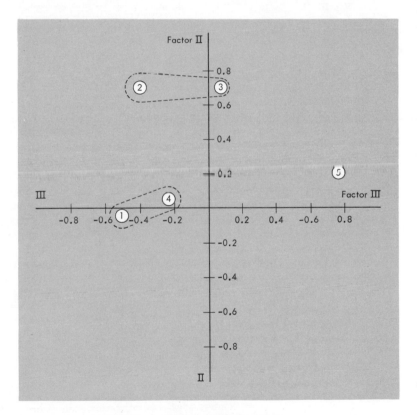

FIG. 4-5 A scatter plot of factor loadings: Factors II and III.

factors, we can plot the loadings in ordinary cartesian space. We can observe from Figure 4-5 that we do not obtain "purity" in the factor load-ings—the condition in which some test loadings group along a single axis but are virtually zero on the other axis. We do note that loadings on tests 2 and 3 and on tests 1 and 4 form clusters. The loading on test 5 is relatively high on Factor III and low on Factor II. While in theory we could add more dimensions (and thus "plot" in 3-space, 4-space, etc.), in practice the illustrated geometrical representation is generalized algebraically.

Factor analysis is a much more complex and lengthy subject than might be indicated by this brief exposition. First, there are many techniques for performing factor analyses (and rotation of axes to more "meaningful" dimensions), and controversy exists over which technique is best. Second, the subjective aspects of factor analysis, e.g., labeling the factors, deciding how many factors to extract, determining when to stop rotation of the factor axes, etc., are subject to many differences in opinion. Third, the computational labor involved in conducting factor analysis (or almost any multivariate technique) necessitates the use of computers.[19]

Application

Factor analysis has been applied to the study of a number of problems besides the ones previously cited. Some examples are:

1. In a study of the determinant of advertising readership, Twedt conducted a factor analysis of thirty-four measures of ad content and layout as a basis for choosing what subset of the thirty-four should be used as independent variables in subsequent regression analysis.[20]

2. In a study of the extent to which brand loyalty varies from one grocery product to another, Farley conducted a factor analysis of nine measures of each market (such as price activity, market share of leading brand, etc.). Based on the results of the factor analysis he replaced the nine original variables in a subsequent regression with three factor scores.[21]

3. Mukherjee conducted a factor analysis of fourteen measures of individual coffee preferences (such as pleasant versus unpleasant flavor, cheap versus expensive taste) as a basis for determining what dimension, if any, underlay the original measures, and, hence, could serve as a better basis for understanding as well as analyzing individual preferences. The original fourteen measures were reduced to four underlying factors.[22]

4. The results of thirteen quality tests for cheddar cheese were factor-analyzed by Harper. Three critical dimensions were identified that could be used as the basis for a quality control program.[23]

[19] For a more complete discussion of factor analysis, see Harry H. Harman, *Modern Factor Analysis* (Chicago: University of Chicago Press, 1960).

[20] Dik Warren Twedt, "A Multiple Factor Analysis of Advertising Readership," *Journal of Applied Psychology*, Vol. 36, No. 3 (June 1952), pp. 207–15.

[21] John V. Farley, "Why Does Brand Loyalty Vary over Products?" *Journal of Marketing Research*, I, No. 4 (November 1964), 9–14.

[22] Bishwa N. Mukherjee, "A Factor Analysis of Some Qualitative Attributes of Coffee," *Journal of Advertising Research*, V, No. 1 (March 1965), 35–38.

[23] Roland Harper, "Factor Analysis as a Technique for Examining Complex Data on Foodstuffs," *Applied Statistics*, V, No. 1 (March 1956), 32–48.

CONCLUDING COMMENTS

The application of multivariate statistical techniques to the analysis of nonexperimental studies will continue to increase in marketing as increased familiarity with the procedures is gained by personnel working in the field. In recent years packaged computer programs have been developed capable of performing the computations required for all of the multivariate techniques discussed in this chapter. The existence and widespread availability of these programs has had the effect of virtually eliminating the computational problems associated with the application of the techniques.

This is especially important in the context of marketing. Given our lack of knowledge of the factors that affect market and customer behavior, it is frequently necessary to conduct exploratory studies based on large masses (large in terms of both number of observations and number of variables) of data. Multivariate techniques provide us with a powerful set of tools for effectively extracting information from large data bases. Man has a hard enough time thinking about the relationships between more than two or three variables at once; to consider 15, 20, or 50 is all but impossible. But by using the computer's computational capabilities, together with the logical procedures embodied in the techniques discussed in this chapter, management can extend its analytical power to formulate and analyze marketing programs and response data.

5

A simulation model is defined as a representation of some real system or operation (such as the market for a given product) which is sufficiently realistic in its structure and content to be used to determine the effects of a complex set of input conditions on the system or to make predictions about the phenomenon under study for eventual test outside the simulation. The

Simulation Studies

art (or, if you prefer, science) of simulation can be viewed as embodying a set of procedures that are complementary to, rather than competitive with, the techniques discussed in the preceding chapters. Simulation models are typically much more complex than those developed on the basis of the aforementioned procedures in that they frequently require the integration of findings from a number of different experimental or nonexperimental studies. In simulation, we attempt to construct an "artificial" world in which we can trace through the consequences of various policies before they are implemented in the real world.

A technique such as simulation, sufficiently flexible to be able to handle complex model formulations, is an extremely important asset to the marketing model builder for two reasons: first, because the solution of a marketing problem often requires the analysis of a large number of environmental factors that are interrelated in a rather complex fashion; and second, because most, if not all, of the measurement techniques and analytical models for the analysis of complete (or near complete) real systems either involve too high a cost to justify their application or are quite inappropriate in terms of the simplicity of their assumption structure. One of the principal advantages of a simulation model is that it can make maximal use of the flexible capabilities of most computer programming languages in creating models of real systems with quite complicated assumption structure.[1]

[1] For a contrast of verbal, mathematical, and logical flow models (of the type easily created, using programming language), see William F. Massy and Jim D. Savvas, "Logical Flow Models for Marketing Analysis," *Journal of Marketing*, XXVIII (January 1964) 30–37.

COMPLEXITY: ANALYTICAL VERSUS SIMULATION MODELS

One of the more significant methodological developments of recent years is the use of Markov process models in the study of consumer behavior. No attempt will be made here to give even a reasonably extensive description of these techniques. Rather, our attention is centered on the use of simulation as a substitute for or complement to the Markovian approach. (The reader who desires an elementary description of Markov process models is referred to Alderson and Green's book.[2] More specialized and extensive discussion may be found in Howard's book [3] and in articles by Frank, Kuehn, and Ehrenberg.[4])

In brief, Markov processes deal with a sequence of events over time which we assume are generated by a probabilistic process; the model is analytical and can be "solved" to yield specifically desired outcomes. The process is called Markovian (after the Russian mathematician Andrei Markov) because the probability of an event is dependent only upon a certain number of immediately preceding outcomes, not on events prior to that.

Suppose a marketing researcher wants to find the probability that a customer will purchase brand A in time period t. He can assume that she was in one of three states when she made her last purchase of the product: (1) she bought brand A; (2) she bought brand B; or (3) she bought brand C, where C stands for all other brands. If he has consumer panel data showing each participant's purchases over some extended period of time, he can estimate *transition probabilities*—the conditional probabilities that a consumer will switch from one state to another, given the outcome of the previous trial. "First-order" Markov processes measure the probability that a consumer will buy brand j on the next purchase occasion, given that she bought brand i on the last purchase occasion. Higher order Markov processes are required if the probability of buying brand j depends on 2, 3, 4, etc., previous purchases.

Table 5-1 presents a set of hypothetical transition probabilities for the preceding occasion. It is read as follows: Given that a customer purchased brand A on her last buying occasion, the estimated probability that she will buy brand A next time is 0.7; that she will switch to brand B is 0.2; that she will switch to some other brand (C) is 0.1. Notice that, since we have utilized a set of mutually exclusive, collectively exhaustive states, all row probabilities sum to unity.

[2] Wroe Alderson and Paul E. Green, *Planning and Problem Solving in Marketing* (Homewood, Ill.: Richard D. Irwin, Inc., 1964).

[3] Ronald A. Howard, *Dynamic Programming and Markov Processes* (Boston: Technology Press of the Massachusetts Institute of Technology, 1960).

[4] Ronald E. Frank, "Brand Choice as a Probability Process," *Journal of Business*, XXXV, No. 1 (January 1962), 43–54; Alfred A. Kuehn, "Consumer Brand Choice as a Learning Process," *Journal of Advertising Research*, II, No. 4 (December 1962), 10–17; and A. S. C. Ehrenberg, "An Appraisal of Markov Brand-Switching Models," *Journal of Marketing Research*, XI (November 1964), 347–62.

TABLE 5-1 Transition Probabilities—Three-State
Illustration

Last purchase	Next purchase			
	A	B	C	Total
A	0.7	0.2	0.1	1.0
B	0.3	0.5	0.2	1.0
C	0.1	0.1	0.8	1.0

To describe the mechanics of a Markov process, let us suppose a customer starts out in state A, that is, as a buyer of brand A, and find the probability that she will be in states A, B, and C, respectively, on the third buying occasion. We could use the methods of matrix algebra to solve the model analytically. For simplicity of discussion, however, we can trace out the process in the tree diagram shown in Figure 5-1. If we performed the necessary multiplication, we would find that after the first, second, and third transitions, the probabilities of our brand A purchaser being a purchaser of brands A, B, and C are as follows:

	A	B	C
First transition	0.7	0.2	0.1
Second transition	0.56	0.25	0.19
Third transition	0.486	0.256	0.258

If we continued to calculate transition probabilities, we would find that they would eventually approach "equilibrium" values; that is, as the number of transitions approached infinity, the probabilities of our purchaser being in states A, B, and C would settle down to a set of fixed values.[5] In this example these values are 0.36, 0.23 and 0.41 for brands A, B, and C, respectively. They are found by solving a set of linear equations.

The problem of interest to the marketer, however, is to *change* the transition probabilities in ways favorable to his firm's brand. The marketer of brand A would like to make the transition probability of state A to state A approach unity; this can be viewed as increasing the "loyalty" measure. Similarly, he would like to increase the probabilities of customers moving from states B and C to state A. These are frequently referred to as "attractiveness" measures. Unfortunately, competitors would like to increase *their* respective "loyalty" and "attractiveness" measures.

The *continual* interplay of competitive strategies results in a *shifting*

---

[5] For a description of how equilibrium values are found, see Alderson and Green, *Planning and Problem Solving in Marketing*, pp. 192–98.

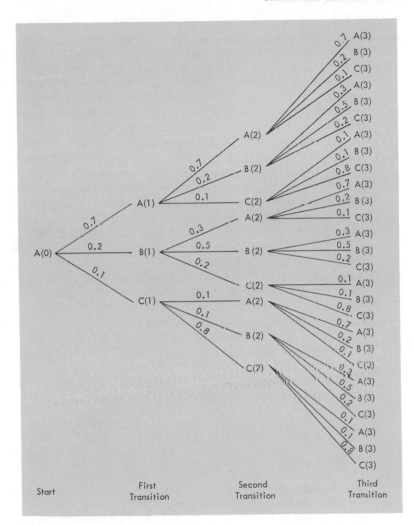

FIG. 5-1 Three-state Markov process.

transition matrix. The application of standard (analytical) Markovian models is considerably complicated in the face of these changes. Furthermore, the model which has thus far been described leaves out a number of important considerations, if it is to serve as a basis for experimenting with alternative marketing strategies. For example, it does not take into account: (1) the time interval between purchases; (2) the amount purchased on each buying occasion; (3) the entry and exit of customers to and from the market; and (4) the link between attitudinal changes and purchasing behavior. While these factors, in and of themselves, make the use of standard models extremely difficult, they represent only a small step toward realism.

Figure 5-2 presents the marketing system for brand A. In the context of this system our model deals exclusively with an analysis of the consumer sector. If we are to capture the "essence" of the entire system, it needs to be substantially broadened to take into account the impact on the transitional matrix of retail price, dealing, advertising, and in-store promotion (shown outside the boxes in Figure 5-2). In addition, it would also be highly desirable to incorporate the *relationship* between manufacturer prices, allowances, and/or shipments and retail behavior such as pricing, advertising, etc. As one expands the list of complicating characteristics that are inherent in the problem of developing a *realistic* model of an entire marketing system, it becomes quickly obvious that standard analytical procedures are not adequate for the task.

For many marketing situations not enough is known about these aforementioned relationships to render a simulation, let alone a Markovian model, useful. However, as shall be discussed in this chapter, some simulations of specific product categories are being or have been developed. However fast (or slow) progress may be, we believe that computer simulation will play an important role as marketing models become more complex, both in their formulation and solution. Simulation has already had a marked impact in more limited problem areas such as physical distribution and media strategy.

SIMULATION: PRO AND CON

The principal advantages of simulation are succinctly summarized by Claycamp and Amstutz:

1. The simulation process can be used to explore the implications of management's perceptions about the external environment. Executives, salesmen, agency personnel, researchers, and other members of the firm's marketing team can pool their intuitive resources and readily available market data in order to come up with a series of statements about the behavior of consumers, middlemen and competitors and the effect of specific marketing actions. Researchers can translate these statements into mathematical and/or logical analogues, and put them together in the form of a simulation. If the process is done well, the output of the simulation has some claim to representing the implications of the perceptual inputs that went into the model. Aberrant results may be traced to errors in the interpretation of manager's statements or, more significantly, to errors or inconsistencies in the original formulations themselves.

2. Simulations can be used to integrate and systematize large quantities of information obtained from past marketing research studies and secondary sources. A model helps to place formerly isolated pieces of data in perspective and often increases the net amount of information that can be obtained from them.

3. A simulation model which has been accepted as a reasonable representation of the real world can be used to guide future research activities. Given confidence in the overall structure of the simulation, the researcher can perform sensitivity analyses with respect to specific

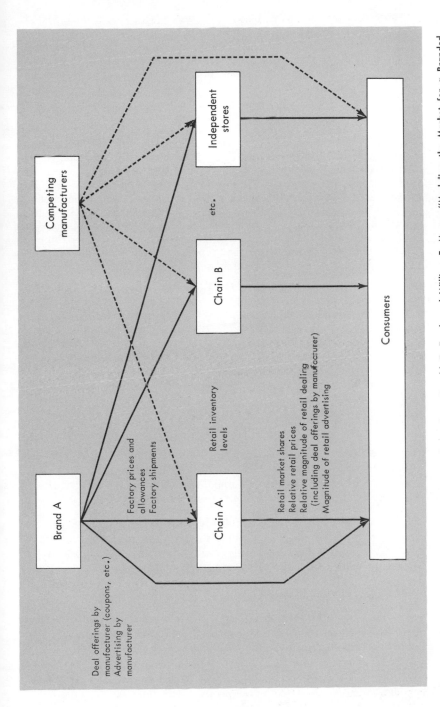

FIG. 5-2 The marketing system for Brand A. Redrawn from Ronald E. Frank and William F. Massy, "Modeling the Market for a Branded, Frequently Purchased Food Product: A Case History," Proceedings of the Seventh TIMS/ORSA Joint Western Regional Meeting, May 1965, p. 96.

parameters or component characteristics. In addition to gaining knowledge about the system's performance characteristics, these tests help to indicate what kinds of additional empirical or theoretical research will have the greatest impact upon the overall accuracy of the model. Research can then be concentrated in areas where potential results are known to be important.

4. Once a market simulation model has been validated to the satisfaction of both research and management personnel, the method of artificial experimentation can be used to derive forecasts of sales levels, market penetration rates, profits, or other criterion variables conditional upon alternative specifications of the elements of the firm's marketing mix. The model can act as a kind of synthetic test market and can be used to screen alternative strategies without incurring the risk or expense of experimentation in the real world. While some experimentation in the real world may always be desirable to settle crucial policy questions and maintain a continuous check on the validity of the simulation, the ability to screen a large number of test candidates through artificial experimentation is likely to produce both substantial savings and better candidates for experimentation in the real environment.[6]

Pitted against these advantages are the following facts:

1. Computer simulation is expensive. The combination of methodological and substantive skills required is costly to create; the amount of computer time required can be substantial; and the model may require the conduct of expensive studies to generate raw data.
2. Computer systems-design problems posed by a simulation can be extremely complex. Seemingly trivial differences in the organization of data files and the order in which computations are performed can make the difference between an efficient simulation system and one that is impractical to operate.
3. Data input procedures must be designed with considerable care so that they will not subsequently inhibit one's ability to use the model for experimental purposes.
4. It is often difficult to develop adequate tests of the validity of the over-all simulation model or its components.

In addition to these limitations, which are more or less idiosyncratic to simulation models, there is another, which simulation models share with simpler models: if important variables are omitted or if the underlying assumptions are inaccurate, one will not obtain valid output.

TYPES OF SIMULATION MODELS

The label *simulation* is associated with a wide variety of different types of modeling activity. The discussion that follows is focused on the following three types of simulation:

[6] H. J. Claycamp and Arnold E. Amstutz, "Simulation Techniques in the Analysis of Marketing Strategy," a paper presented at Purdue University, July 1966, at a symposium on Applications of the Sciences in Marketing. Mimeographed, pp. 5-7.

(1) _Monte Carlo_ methods represent one of the oldest uses of simulation in dealing with complex probabilistic processes. These techniques are akin to using random sampling to explore the properties of probabilistic (and sometimes nonstatistical) models.

(2) _Heuristic programming_ is applied to the development of "rules of thumb" or heuristics for solving problems that are not tractable by standard analytical methods. The simulation attempts to reproduce the decision rules that human problem solvers appear to use. The techniques of heuristic programming have been applied to a surprisingly diverse set of activities, ranging from assembly-line balancing [7] to warehouse location [8] to investment portfolio selection.[9]

(3) _Experimental and business gaming_ are two variations of operational gaming simulations where the actions of human players represent a part of the process being simulated. Business games range from simple pencil-and-paper games to highly complex, computerized games for making strategic-level decisions; they are designed primarily for educational purposes. Experimental games, on the other hand, are designed for research; their purpose is to observe the behavior of subjects in a simulated environment. Because of the objective of this book, only experimental gaming is discussed in this chapter.

We have focused on the three types of simulations which, in our opinion, are of the greatest relative importance to understanding and policy formulation across a broad spectrum of marketing problems. Each type (especially Monte Carlo and heuristic programming) contains logical components out of which a simulation model may be built, but in practice the categories do overlap to some degree. For example, Monte Carlo procedures are often used in conjunction with heuristic programming techniques.

Monte Carlo Methods

Monte Carlo techniques are essentially experimental sampling techniques for dealing with either (1) processes that are essentially probabilistic or (2) deterministic processes that can be approximated by probabilistic ones. We shall confine our remarks entirely to the first (and more often used) application.

In order to illustrate the use of Monte Carlo in its simplest terms, let us suppose that we are interested in finding the average length of a line between any two random points on the unit line zero to one, using a large sample of points. It so happens that this problem has an exact analytical solution, namely one-third. Suppose, however, that we did not

[7] Fred M. Tonge, _A Heuristic Program for Assembly-Line Balancing_ (Englewood Cliffs, N. J.: Prentice-Hall, Inc., 1961).

[8] Alfred A. Kuehn and Michael J. Hamburger, "A Heuristic Program for Locating Warehouses," _Management Science,_ IX (July 1963), 643–66.

[9] Geoffrey P. E. Clarkson, _Portfolio Selection: A Simulation of Trust Investment_ (Englewood Cliffs, N. J.: Prentice-Hall, Inc., 1962).

know the solution and desired to obtain a *numerical estimate* by means of Monte Carlo. Operationally we would consult a table of random numbers. Suppose we desired to use only two-digit numbers and that the first two random numbers shown in the table were 94 and 75. Since the points must fall in the 0–1 interval, we call these values 0.94 and 0.75, respectively.

Table 5-2 shows an illustrative sampling of points (and their distance difference) for this problem. The first two entries, 0.94 and 0.75, were the first two random numbers drawn; the distance between them is 0.19. Similarly, the distance between the second pair of points, 0.53 and 0.14, is 0.39, and so on. The arithmetic mean of this sample of 24 paired differences is $(0.19 + 0.39 + \cdots + 0.13) \div 24 = 0.253$. As we might

TABLE 5-2 Illustration of Monte Carlo in Approximating the Expected Length of a Line in the Range 0–1

First point	Second point	Distance	First point	Second point	Distance	First point	Second point	Distance
0.94	0.75	0.19	0.02	0.07	0.05	0.18	0.74	0.56
0.53	0.14	0.39	0.26	0.25	0.01	0.66	0.67	0.01
0.57	0.60	0.03	0.61	0.96	0.35	0.59	0.04	0.55
0.96	0.64	0.32	0.54	0.69	0.15	0.01	0.54	0.53
0.43	0.65	0.22	0.77	0.97	0.20	0.39	0.09	0.30
0.65	0.39	0.26	0.13	0.02	0.11	0.88	0.69	0.19
0.82	0.39	0.43	0.93	0.91	0.02	0.25	0.01	0.24
0.91	0.19	0.72	0.86	0.74	0.12	0.47	0.34	0.13

expect, because of sampling error, we have only approximated the "true" expectation (based on an infinitely large sample). In practice we might wish to increase our sample for greater accuracy or to set up confidence intervals about our sample mean (that is, to treat the artifacts as they would be treated in real-world sampling situations).

The preceding illustration is a rather trivial example of the use of Monte Carlo procedures. We can, however, increase the complexity of the problem formulation for dealing with situations that come closer to the real-world conditions. This is shown in the following example.

Drug Marketing Strategy: An Example. One of the most elaborate Monte Carlo simulations to date was developed by Claycamp and Amstutz.[10] Its objective was to develop a synthetic test market of the prescription-drug field in sufficient detail to enable management to test the effects of alternative marketing strategies without having to invest the time and expense required to conduct comparable studies in its real environment. Management was primarily interested in using the model to:

[10] The description that follows is paraphrased from Claycamp and Amstutz, *op. cit.*, pp. 21–37.

1. Evaluate the effectiveness of promotional media
2. Evaluate the effectiveness of the sales force (detail men)
3. Test alternative policies and strategies for marketing particular products to a given market segment
4. Evaluate the probable success of new products at an early stage of market development
5. Assess the validity of management's understanding of the dynamics of the prescription-drug marketing system.

Figure 5-3 presents the macro specification for the prescription drug market. This chart presents the flow of product (P), information (I), and orders (O) between the various parties represented in the simulation. Though competing firms are not reported in Figure 5-3, they are considered in detail in the actual simulation. To illustrate the logic of the diagram, we shall trace the product flow. Starting in the upper left corner, the product flows from the company to wholesalers and doctors. From the wholesalers it can go to their detail men, doctors, pharmacies, and hospitals, and from each of these parties (with the exception of detail men) to patients.

Based on this configuration of parties, the actual simulation consists of a population of doctors, each of whom is represented by a "file," a magnetic tape that includes such information as his specialization, geographic region, patient load, the probability that he will receive and be exposed to information from various media and companies, as well as the seasonal distribution of each "indication" (e.g., polio or mumps) of interest, etc.

One doctor's behavior is simulated at a time, in the manner described briefly in the following paragraphs. Once the last doctor has been processed, a summary report is written which provides measures of such things as drug usage by company and brand that resulted from the particular configuration of inputs (detail men's activity, advertising, etc.) for each company as well as the configuration of symptoms that occurred during the time period.

Doctor File Input. Each simulated doctor is described by the content of a doctor file record. Doctor files are recorded on tape sequentially by geographic region. A single doctor file is held in [the computer's] core at a given point in time. After simulating the doctor's activity for a specified number of weeks, the file is updated to reflect his experiences and written on tape. A new doctor is then read into core, and the procedure is repeated.

The Time Loop. The system is structured so that time is moved past each doctor in turn. This organization of the system is necessitated by the large size of the doctor file record which makes it impractical to move doctors in and out of core or to maintain more than one doctor in core at a given point in time.

During most simulation runs, the time period considered is one simulated year. The time step is one week and the time index (IT)

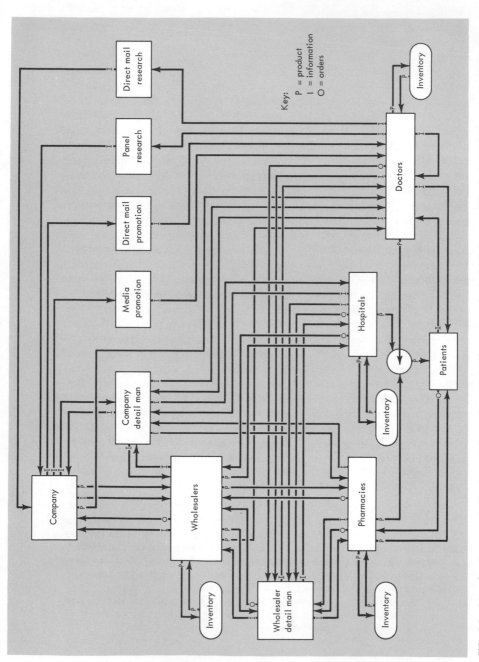

FIG. 5-3 Example of macro specifications. Redrawn from H. J. Claycamp and Arnold E. Amstutz, "Simulation Techniques in the Analysis of Marketing Strategy," a paper presented at Purdue University, July 1966, at a symposium on Applications of the Sciences in Marketing.

proceeds sequentially from 1 through 52. Events occurring during a particular week are identified by a monotonic date code which, during processing of the simulation, is referenced to the time index (IT).

Doctor Response to Media Promotion. During each week in simulated time, the publication frequency of each relevant journal is tested to determine whether it is published during the week under consideration. If a particular journal appears, the probability of the doctor then under consideration being exposed to that journal is developed. If, on the basis of this probability it is determined that the doctor will be exposed to the journal, each advertisement appearing in an advertisement schedule table for that journal is examined to determine whether or not the doctor will be exposed to, and assimilate, any new information. When an advertisement is assimilated, the doctor's response to the message is established and his memory updated to take account of information content. This process is continued for all media, messages, and doctors at each point in time.

Direct Mail Response. The handling of direct mail response is structured in a manner analogous to media promotion. During each simulated week, a comparison is made to determine whether any direct mail pieces appear. If a direct mail piece is being sent during the week in question, exposure probabilities are developed to determine whether or not the particular doctor then being considered will be exposed to the specified mailing. If exposure occurs, assimilation probabilities are generated and, if on the basis of these probabilities it is determined that the doctor will assimilate portions of the communication, his response is determined and his memory updated.

Response to Salesman Detail. In developing a representation of the doctor's response to salesman communication, the probability of exposure is first determined on the basis of parameter values in the doctor file record which establish the probability that the doctor will receive a call from a salesman representing any one of the relevant companies. If the doctor is exposed to a salesman from a particular company, the schedule of details (sales messages for a specific drug) presented by that salesman is examined to determine which details are being presented to doctors of the indicated specialty during the week under consideration. If a particular detail is presented and assimilation occurs, the doctor memory is updated. As in the case of all other communication response loops, this procedure continues until all sales messages have been considered.

Response to Convention Activity. Exposure to presentations at a convention is based on a convention schedule which specifies the probability of a doctor of a particular specialty and residence attending a convention held at a particular time. In keeping with the previously established procedure, the convention schedule is examined once each simulated week to determine whether or not a convention is being held. If a convention is being held, the probability of the doctor then in core attending that convention is determined and, if the doctor is found to attend the convention, procedures similar to those outlined above are used to determine exposure and assimilation of relevant information.

Response to Word-of-Mouth Communication. Within the structure of the simulation, messages generated by doctors in a particular region are accumulated along with descriptors of the generating doctor in a table of word-of-mouth messages. Thus, when a particular doctor is in core, messages generated at various points in time by doctors preceding him are available in the word-of-mouth table. This table is referenced in a manner analogous to the schedule and content table discussed for other media. The probability of interaction between the doctor in core and the message-generating doctor who preceded him is established. If the doctor is exposed to the word-of-mouth communication, the probability of assimilation is developed in a manner analogous to other communication functions and the doctor's memory is updated to reflect the word-of-mouth interaction.

Treatment of Patients. The simulated doctor is exposed to patients from an artificial patient population which is supplied as an input to the simulation. An average patient load parameter in each doctor file record determines how many patients will be treated in a given week. In treating a patient the simulated doctor determines what drug or drugs, if any, will be prescribed for the exhibited indication(s) of the patient.

Once treatment has been decided upon the probability that it will achieve desired results is established on the basis of clinical data. If it is determined that the treatment undertaken will not prove effective within a specified period of time, the patient is maintained in a backlog of patients who will return to the doctor at some time in the future. If the outcome of treatment is successful, the patient is for all practical purposes dropped from the model. In either instance, the trial and outcome (including possible side effects) of a particular treatment is noted.

After the first simulated week the doctor has two sources of patients: (1) patients in the population from which his original patient group was drawn; and (2) patients who require continuing treatment. During subsequent time periods the doctor's first source of patients is the returning patient file. After all patients previously treated and scheduled to return have been treated, the doctor considers new patients from the outside population.

Generation of Word-of-Mouth Communication. As the doctor considers various drugs in context of the treatment during the simulated week, a record of his attitude toward his experiences is maintained. Following completion of the treatment cycle for a particular simulated week, this record is examined to determine whether the doctor will generate word-of-mouth communication regarding some aspect of his recent treatment experience. If such word-of-mouth communication is generated, communication content is established, dated, and stored in the word-of-mouth communication file for later referencing by other doctors.

Forgetting. At certain prescribed time intervals, the doctor's memory is examined to determine whether forgetting would have occurred during the lapsed time period. The memory record for each drug is examined and, if forgetting has occurred, the record is reduced.

Time Cycle Combination. The basic process described above is repeated for each week in the simulated year for each doctor in the artificial population. Once the final week for a given doctor is completed, an activity report is generated and the doctor file record is updated to reflect his experiences during the simulated year. This record is then written on tape to serve as an input for simulation of future time periods.

Following completion of a given doctor record, another doctor record is read from the tape file and the process described is repeated. After all doctors have been considered for the specified period of simulated time, a final summary report is written and the simulation terminates.[11]

Although this description provides an insight into the logical structure and flow of the drug-market simulation model, it nonetheless is extremely superficial. Extremely elaborate models of doctor behavior are required to make the total simulation perform in a reliable manner. Models of the same type have also been developed to study the effects of economic policy on the American economy [12] and of alternative media schedules on the reach and pattern of customer exposures.[13]

Heuristic Programming

Heuristic programming is a branch of simulation that has as its objective the reproduction of decision processes used by human problem solvers. Heuristics are "rules of thumb" that often can produce "acceptable" solutions where optimal solutions could be found, if at all, only by costly analytical models. Consider, for example, the development of an "optimal" strategy for playing chess. A good player might be able to plan three or four moves ahead by rejecting outright whole classes of inferior moves. Although in theory one could develop a program to evaluate *all* possible moves, it is clear that such an endeavor would be impractical because of the sheer number of alternatives that would have to be evaluated. A heuristic program for class playing would attempt to use a "seasoned player's" rules of thumb as a partial basis for choosing a *satisfactory* strategy. Using heuristics, one does not attempt to find a *best* (or optimal) solution but, instead, a *satisfactory* one consistent with the cost of developing better alternatives.

In an interesting example of heuristic programming,[14] Clarkson interviewed and observed the investment behavior of a group of trust investors. Using his data, he was able to design a computer simulation which led to quite good predictions of the trust officers' actual security selections from data not included in the original formulation of the simulation. Robinson has reported a simulation in which, by determining the decision rules which supervisors used in conducting daily warehouse operations, a model was designed to test alternative policies regarding

[11] *Ibid.*, pp. 31–37. Quoted with minor revision.

[12] Guy H. Orcutt, *et al., Microanalysis of Socioeconomic Systems: A Simulation Study* (New York: Harper and Row, Publishers, 1961).

[13] *Simulmatics Media-Mix: Technical Description* (New York: The Simulmatics Corporation, October 1962).

[14] *Portfolio Selection: A Simulation of Trust Investment.*

warehouse operation.[15] Here again, emphasis was on *reproducing the* actual decision process, whether or not optimal, in order to have a base for general study and possible improvement.

In the following paragraphs two heuristic simulations will be described. The first was designed to provide a basis for determining warehouse locations, while the second was a study of the pricing behavior of department store buyers.

Warehouse Location. Kuehn and Hamburger have developed a model for determining the geographic pattern of warehouse location, based on a balancing of transportation cost, operation cost, and the incremental profits associated with increases in the speed of delivery to the customer. A flow diagram presenting the logical structure of their program is shown in Figure 5-4. The program is divided into two parts: (1) *the main program,* which locates warehouses one at a time until no additional ones can be added without increasing total costs; and (2) the "bump-and-shift" routine, which attempts to modify the distribution network arrived at in the main programming by evaluating the profit implications of dropping warehouses or of shifting them from one location to another. Boxes 1–7 in the flow diagram correspond to the main program, while box 8 represents the bump-and-shift routine.

The principal heuristics used in the main program are as follows:

1. Most geographic locations are not promising sites for a regional warehouse; locations with promise will be at or near concentrations of demand. The use of this heuristic permits concentration on less than 1/100 of 1 per cent of the total land area of the United States as a basis for possible locations.

2. Near optimum warehousing systems can be developed by locating warehouses one at a time, adding at each stage of the analysis that warehouse which produces the greatest cost savings for the entire system.

3. Only a small proportion of all possible warehouses need be evaluated in detail at each stage of the analysis in order to determine the next warehouse site to be added. The heuristic used for screening calls for N of the M potential warehouse locations (see step 3, Figure 5-4). The N potential warehouse sites chosen at each stage are those which, considering only local demand, would result in the greatest cost savings (or smallest increase in costs) if serviced by a local warehouse rather than by the system existing in the previous stage (see step 2, Figure 5-4). In other words, it is assumed that at any stage we can do reasonably well by locating the next warehouse in one of the N areas chosen on the basis of local demand and related warehousing and transportation costs.[16]

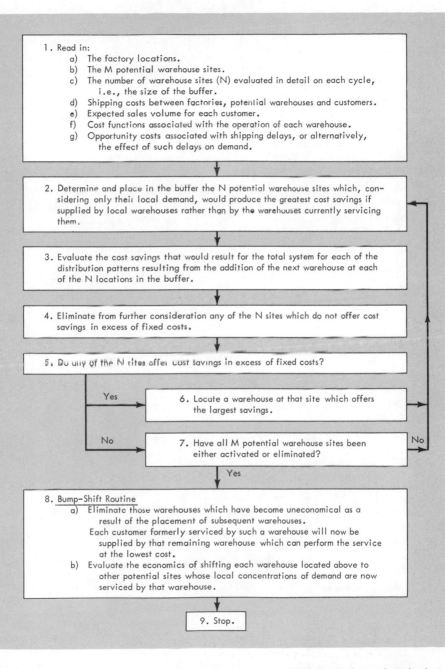

1. Read in:
    a) The factory locations.
    b) The M potential warehouse sites.
    c) The number of warehouse sites (N) evaluated in detail on each cycle,
       i.e., the size of the buffer.
    d) Shipping costs between factories, potential warehouses and customers.
    e) Expected sales volume for each customer.
    f) Cost functions associated with the operation of each warehouse.
    g) Opportunity costs associated with shipping delays, or alternatively,
       the effect of such delays on demand.

2. Determine and place in the buffer the N potential warehouse sites which, considering only their local demand, would produce the greatest cost savings if
   supplied by local warehouses rather than by the warehouses currently servicing
   them.

3. Evaluate the cost savings that would result for the total system for each of the
   distribution patterns resulting from the addition of the next warehouse at each
   of the N locations in the buffer.

4. Eliminate from further consideration any of the N sites which do not offer cost
   savings in excess of fixed costs.

5. Do any of the N sites offer cost savings in excess of fixed costs?

Yes

6. Locate a warehouse at that site which offers
   the largest savings.

No

7. Have all M potential warehouse sites been
   either activated or eliminated?

No

Yes

8. Bump-Shift Routine
    a) Eliminate those warehouses which have become uneconomical as a
       result of the placement of subsequent warehouses.
       Each customer formerly serviced by such a warehouse will now be
       supplied by that remaining warehouse which can perform the service
       at the lowest cost.
    b) Evaluate the economics of shifting each warehouse located above to
       other potential sites whose local concentrations of demand are now
       serviced by that warehouse.

9. Stop.

FIG. 5-4 Flow diagram for warehouse location. Redrawn from Alfred A. Kuehn and Michael J. Hamburger, "A Heuristic Program for Locating Warehouses," *Management Science*, IX (July 1963), 647.

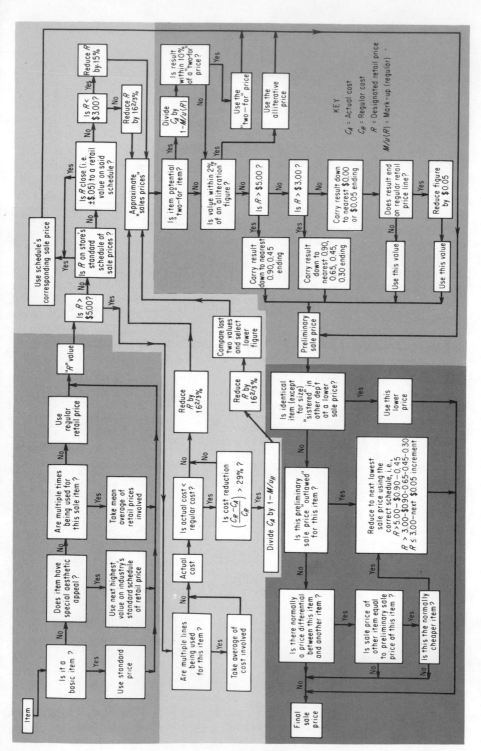

FIG. 5-5 Flow chart for sale pricing decisions. Redrawn from Richard M. Cyert and James G. March, *A Behavioral Theory of the Firm* (Englewood Cliffs, N. J.: Prentice-Hall, Inc., 1963), p. 141.

The task of the bump-and-shift routine is to modify the solution arrived at by the main program in one of the following two ways:

1. It eliminates warehouses that are no longer economical because customers originally served by them can be more economically served by warehouses that were subsequently located.
2. It evaluates the effect of shifting warehouses from their present location to other locations within their territories.

The results reported by Kuehn and Hamburger support the conclusion that heuristic programming results compare favorably to those generated by Monte Carlo simulation or by formal analytical models such as linear programming.

Department Store Pricing. Cyert and March conducted an intensive study of the ordering and pricing behavior in one department of a large retail department store which was part of an oligopolistic market consisting of three large downtown stores. Though each store also operated one or more suburban stores, the focus of this study was on the downtown market. To be more specific, the researchers attempted to build a simulation model of the decision-making process (in one department) used to set sale prices, markups, and markdowns.

The nature of their model is illustrated in Figure 5-5, which reports the logical flow of sale-pricing decisions. Figure 5-5 actually consists of four blocks of logic representing the four major stages in the decision-making process for sale pricing—namely, the determination of:

1. The regular price for an item
2. The approximate sale price
3. The actual sale price rounded to the nearest "traditional" pricing category (e.g., $1.44 would be rounded to $1.45)
4. The internal consistency of the price for the item under consideration with such things as the normal price differential between it and other items in the same department or in other departments

The performance of the simulation in predicting sale price and markdown and markup decisions for new items (items not used as the basis for building the model) was quite impressive. Of a total of 58 sale price predictions, the model predicted 56 correctly to the penny. The batting average for markups was 188 out of 197, while that for markdowns was 140 out of 159.

This simulation and the one by Clarkson mentioned earlier represent important advances in the study of managerial decision-making behavior. They present a new approach to the understanding and for the eventual improvement of decision-making practices. Conceivably it may be possible for sufficiently realistic models to be built so that many repetitive decisions can be made by the computer.

Experimental Gaming

The third type of simulation with which we shall be concerned is also gaining increasing attention in marketing. Experimental gaming is used primarily for research and is thus distinguishable from business gaming, which is designed as an educational tool. Its purpose is to test in an artificial environment certain hypotheses about human behavior that, because of the complexity of the real world and the difficulty of control, cannot easily be tested under ongoing conditions.

As an illustration of experimental gaming, Pessemier has reported on a series of simulated shopping trips in which subjects were given assortments of goods (toothpaste, toilet soaps) at various prices. A principal objective of the game was to see at what price differentials subjects would switch from the brand they preferred to one they like less. With regard to the "realism" of such experiments, Pessemier states:

> The personal experience of the buyer of consumer goods is easy to describe. He seeks to satisfy his wants by purchasing goods from existing institutions and assortments and he has limited time, information and funds to use in gaining these ends. By the acts of gathering satisfactions in the market, he is expressing personal judgments about the relative value of what the market has to offer. When taken over a given period of time, the sum of the preference-motivated actions of all buyers represents demand. In other words, within the limits of the consumer's capacity to act, demand for a product depends on how consumers evaluate the product's relative worth.
>
> Since in the market it is often difficult to determine the demands or preferences for branded products over a moderate range of price variation, the question naturally arises: Can it be done in a controlled environment? An affirmative answer can be given provided the buyer can be placed in a position where the consequences of his actions in the experimental environment will have an impact on his well-being and conduct similar to what they would have in the market: the experimental conditions should be *psychologically equivalent* to the market, not necessarily physically identical. If the experimental situation is made "real" by duplicating those aspects of the market which influence buyer action, then the experimental results will closely parallel the decisions made by consumers confronted by similar conditions in everyday life.[17]

In other words, although experimental gaming may lack realism, its results, once understood, can lead to some generalization. The study of actual behavior in the marketplace, in contrast, is undoubtedly more realistic, but it is so complex that it renders understanding of the phenomena (and their generalization over a variety of conditions) extremely difficult. Ideally, of course, the hypotheses "tested" under experimental

[17] Reprinted from Edgar A. Pessemier's "An Experimental Method of Estimating Demand," *Journal of Business*, XXXIII, No. 4 (October 1960), 373–74, by permission of The University of Chicago Press.

gaming conditions should be subjected to additional tests in more realistic environments. In practice, however, such a stepwise progression is hard to make inasmuch as the experimenter's ability to control (or measure) the influence of external variables rapidly diminishes as his "laboratory" comes closer to the actual marketplace.

In the following paragraphs we shall describe two experimental games which are focused on the study of the same phenomenon, brand choice, but which vary in the degree of realism built into the experimental situation.

Green, Halbert and Robinson conducted an experiment to explore the following questions:

1. Do subjects typified as "brand switchers" tend to be more active acquirers of information than do subjects typified as "brand-loyal"?
2. How are tendencies toward information acquisition related to the payoff distributions associated with the possible brand choices and the cost of acquiring information?
3. How do subjects who have become brand-loyal react to the appearance of a new brand?
4. Do some subjects develop brand loyalties even when there are no differences in the payoff distributions?
5. Is game performance associated with certain personality variables, and can both sets of variables—game behavior and personality characteristics—be useful in predicting brand-choice behavior in the real world?

Seventy-two Philadelphia housewives participated in the experiment. In addition to playing "the game" each subject filled out questionnaires that provided information on store loyalty, brand awareness and loyalty for various product classes, a self-evaluation of ability to perceive differences among brands, and measures of personality characteristics.

Each subject played a series of games based on the following instructions:

> "We would like to enlist your cooperation in a series of experiments dealing with decision making under uncertainty. As a housewife who serves as 'purchasing agent' for your family, you no doubt are faced almost daily with a variety of brands available for any product class, ranging from food items to appliances. Naturally you would like to choose that particular brand which results in the 'greatest satisfaction' for each sum of money spent.
>
> "Here are three urns labeled A, B and C. Each urn contains a fixed number of poker chips with numbers written on them, such as +2, −1, 0, +3, and so forth. [The subject was then shown a demonstration urn—not used in the games—and was invited to look at the numbered poker chips.]
>
> "For purposes of this experiment, assume that the urns represent brands in a particular product class. We are going to give you $6.00 in silver. [A stack of change totaling $6.00 was placed in front of the

subject.] Naturally you would like to spend this money in the best way possible. As a matter of fact, the final payment to your organization will be proportioned to the amount of money you have left after all exercises are over. If, during any experiment, you should run out of money, we will lend you additional funds.

"In this experiment, urns A and B represent the first two 'brands' available for choice. Later on we shall introduce the new 'brand,' urn C. Buying a brand, that is, selecting a chip from the available urns, costs one quarter. You will receive the number of quarters—minus, zero, or plus—indicated on the chip which you choose from the urn of your choice. This chip will then be returned to the urn from which it was drawn, and the urn will be shaken up to keep the chips well mixed. Your net benefit will therefore be this number of quarters less the one quarter required to purchase a brand.

"In a real shopping trip it is frequently possible for you to obtain some information as to the comparative benefits of each brand by means of looking at advertising, subscribing to consumer reports, asking your neighbors, or buying the brand on a trial basis. You can similarly obtain information in this experiment.

"Before any buying trial—including the first—you will be able to purchase as many chips as you wish from any urn available for choice. These chips can be taken, in any combination, from each urn. Each chip will cost you 10 cents to see. After you have decided how many —if any—chips you wish to see from each urn, you may select them yourself and note the numbers that appear on them. These chips will then be returned to their respective urns.

"You must then decide which urn you wish to choose for 'buying' purposes. On any 'buying' occasion only one of the urns available for choice can be chosen. After you pay your quarter and choose a chip from the urn of your choice, you will receive the number of quarters written on the chip if the number is preceded by a plus sign. If the number is zero, you receive nothing. If the number is preceded by a minus sign you must pay to us the number so indicated. This is, of course, in addition to the quarter you paid for the opportunity to purchase the 'brand.' The chip is then returned to the urn from which it was selected.

"You are then ready to make another information-buying decision, if you care to before making another purchase. Each trial of the game will proceed according to this plan.

"Later on in the game the new 'brand,' urn C, will become available for choice. You then have three possibilities for information buying and three possibilities for 'brand buying.'

"Remember this. On each information-buying trial, you must state in advance how many chips you wish to purchase from any urn available for choice. Then you must make a purchasing choice—of one urn —from among those available. You then proceed to a new trial until the game is over. Your objective, of course, is to try to determine which urn is paying off best in order to end up with as much money as you can, since the actual amount of money you receive will be based on your money holdings at the end of the game.[18]

[18] Paul E. Green, Michael H. Halbert, and Patrick J. Robinson, "Experimental Gaming in Consumer Brand Choice Behavior," *The Business Quarterly* (Fall 1965), pp. 50–51.

Based on an analysis of the results of the game, the authors concluded that:

1. Housewives who had a high propensity to switch brands tended to acquire more information in the game setting than did subjects classified as "loyal."
2. Brand loyalties developed even in games in which the "brands" were identical.
3. Game playing variables and personality test scores appeared to predict classification of subjects as "loyal" or as "switchers" only moderately well.

As the authors readily admit, one of the limitations of their work is the lack of realism in the gaming situation.

Another experiment on the subject of brand loyalty, reported by Tucker, had somewhat more realism.[19] On twelve consecutive occasions each of 42 housewives was asked to choose from a tray one of four brands of bread identical except for the lettering on the labels. The position of the brands on the tray was rotated, using a Latin square design so that no brand occupied the same position two times in a row and so that each brand occupied the same position with equal frequency. The strength of brand loyalty was determined as follows: After a housewife had picked the same brand on three consecutive trials, the price of the brand she had picked most frequently prior to those trials was reduced by a penny.

Based on Tucker's definition, if no brand loyalty were present, one would expect 25 per cent of each housewife's purchases to be made for each brand. By the end of the experiment a number of customers became "brand loyal" even though there was no discernible difference between the brands other than their name. In addition, during the first few trials less loyalty than one would expect by chance was shown. Housewives tended to switch unusually often from one brand to another on consecutive trials. This appears to be the result of an initial period of search among the four alternatives before actually settling on one or more.

Experimental games do offer promise as a tool for the study of behavior. However, at this point in their development little is known about the "rules of translation" for moving from laboratory to real-world situations.

PRESENT LIMITATIONS AND FUTURE TRENDS

A major problem facing model builders in marketing is a *lack of understanding of the descriptive part of the model.* It is one thing to *postulate* a response function of sales to changes in advertising expenditures and then to solve the model. It is quite another thing to *measure* the response function and arrive at a realistic description of sales behavior with respect to advertising changes. The pioneering builders of simulation

[19] W. T. Tucker, "The Development of Brand Loyalty," *Journal of Marketing Research*, I (August 1964), 32–35.

models were content to pick relationships that looked "reasonable" and then to solve the model on the basis of little or no data at all.

The applications that can be made of current marketing models, simulation or otherwise, are severely limited by our lack of understanding of marketing *relationships*. In our judgment realistic models in marketing will have to take into account, to an increasing extent, the problems of measurement and interaction. We discuss these limitations in terms of (1) interaction phenomena and (2) nonstationary characteristics of marketing systems.

Interaction Phenomena in Marketing

There are a large number of courses of action typically available to the firm in selecting, for example, the appropriate mix of sales effort—advertising, personal selling, pricing, distribution, and marketing and technical service. Most of the models we have discussed have decoupled one part of the problem from other parts. For example, a number of warehouse-location models have been developed. But the effectiveness of a given system of warehousing may, of course, be dependent on the configuration of intermediate sellers between the manufacturer and the ultimate consumer, and most of the models do not take this into account.

Most of the models make either no assumptions or very naïve ones about competitors' actions. How "optimal" is a so-called optimization model if competitors are using similar techniques? This question has received virtually no attention at all. Rather, all of the models we have discussed suffer from the danger of "incomplete" optimization. Of course, a fully comprehensive system is an unattainable ideal. What we would like to do, however, is to increase the realism of models to encompass variables not heretofore included, or at least to develop policies that are not highly sensitive to factors not under the firm's control.

Some activities are under way which are addressed to the problems enumerated above. To an increasing extent, firms are using, statistically designed field experiments in which components of the sales effort mix are systematically varied over space or time for the purpose of estimating the response "surface" of sales (and/or intermediate variables, such as awareness, recall, etc., which are assumed to be correlated with sales) to changes in amount and type of sales effort. In short, current activity appears to be emphasizing *systematic measurement procedures* for determining response functions under a variety of conditions. Controlled experimentation and regression analysis represent major activities on the part of firms who have passed the "naïve" stage of model formulation.

Less work is being done on the development of interactive models that explore the "optimality" of various models under varying environmental conditions with regard to competitors', distributors', and consumers' reactions. There is reason to believe, however, that computer simulation will be used to an increasing extent in exploring the "robustness" of various models under alternative environmental conditions.

In summary, the model builder has started to recognize the limitations of previous optimization techniques, the need to establish functional relationships ("well-behaved," in a mathematical sense, or not) through controlled experimentation, and the value of exploring the model's behavior under a variety of environmental conditions. Simulation models will become increasingly appropriate as these complexities are added.

Ultimately, of course, we would like to understand buying behavior, not merely measure its sales effects through controlled experimentation. For example, Markov processes—with all of their limitations—have been proposed as the basis for a "model" of customer brand switching. We have already discussed some of the model's inadequacies and the need to develop more realistic simulations. In this area of interest, current research in simulation, market measurement, and experimental gaming may shed light on the development of explanatory—not merely predictive—models of market behavior.

Nonstationary Characteristics of Marketing Systems

Another major problem facing the model builder in marketing is the seeming lack of stability of relationships over time. (We have already encountered this problem in our discussion of some of the criticisms that have been leveled against Markov brand-switching models. For example, will sales-advertising relationships, which have been measured by time-consuming and costly experimentation, be stable enough to persist into the next period(s) when, presumably, the firm will act upon the experimental findings?)

It has often been said that marketing is characterized by instability; that, in fact, it is the objective of advertising managers, sales managers, and new-product managers to upset the status quo in an attempt to increase the firm's market share and profit position. Can the model builder ever hope to predict the effects of courses of action in the light of policies dedicated to change?

All prediction, however, is based upon the assumption of some type of stability in the system under study. The terms *static* and *dynamic* are relative. For example, a trend equation predicting sales in the next period is making a "dynamic" forecast; but the analyst assumes that the values of the parameters in the model being used to predict sales are stable over the forecast period. Similarly, a researcher may design a model for predicting changes in the transition probabilities of a Markov process model. The transition probabilities predicted by such a model are "nonstationary," but the model itself is not. What the researcher has done is to develop a "super-model" for predicting changes in "lower-level" models.

The point to be made is that the model builder is free to choose the level of the process which he assumes to be stable and can thereby formulate "super" and "super-super" decision rules which will show stability in processes that, at lower levels, appear to be rapidly changing in some unpredictable manner. This is not to say, of course, that the construction of such higher-level models is currently, or will be, an easy task. It is to say, however, that the argument that "everything is changing too fast to analyze" is not necessarily correct. If the process exhibits instability at *all* levels which the analyst can conceive, then there is little to be gained in trying to predict the system's output; it would be akin to trying to predict the next digit in a random number sequence. Fortunately, we "have faith" that systems, at some level, exhibit sufficient stability for us to make useful predictions; finding this level, of course, may be another matter, but the quest represents an exciting area for future research.

Part Three

A LOOK TO THE FUTURE

6

In our opinion, decision theory, multivariate statistical techniques (as applied to experimental and nonexperimental studies), and simulation models are in the process of becoming as important to the conduct of marketing research as sampling theory or the procedures used in designing questionnaires are at present. Increasingly, the question that confronts manager and

Future Developments

researcher alike is not whether quantitative techniques should be used, but how to best make use of them in dealing with a specific problem. In this chapter, we first discuss the limitations of the current state of the art and then speculate on the nature of future progress in terms of extensions of technique.

PRESENT LIMITATIONS

If published studies represent actual practice, very few companies have adopted decision theory as a framework for appraising the value of marketing research, let alone as one for guiding the allocation of research resources among competing activities.[1] Part of this lag in application is to be expected, for the diffusion of new methodology often takes several years to appear in the form of routine application. But there are some important methodological problems which have limited application. First, little is known about the validity and reliability of prior information supplied by "predictive experts," that is, the information incorporated into the Bayesian model as "prior" probabilities. Second, we need to know more about how organizations form goals, how they develop trade-offs among conflicting goals, and how stable the decision maker's goal structure remains over time.

In Chapters 3 and 4 we analyzed various experimental and nonexperimental studies, respectively. While statistically designed experiments represent a way to develop appropriate response functions to changes in the amount and kind of marketing effort, the applica-

---

[1] For a survey of the literature, see Paul E. Green and Ronald E. Frank, "Bayesian Statistics and Marketing Research," *Applied Statistics*, XV (November 1966), 173–89.

tion of these procedures is both time-consuming and expensive. Serious attempts need to be made to determine their value. In particular, studies should be made of the stability over space and time of different types of behavior on the part of consumers, middlemen, and competitors. Unless there is a systematic element that is discernible over time, behavioral instability will decrease the value of either experimental or nonexperimental analyses. In addition, most of the applications to date have assumed linear relationships among the variables under study. Is linearity a sufficiently accurate approximation of the nature of the underlying relationships? More work needs to be done to find out.

In Chapter 5 we discussed mathematical models, principally simulation models. Most of the current models make very simplifying assumptions about competitive behavior and the influence of the firm's other courses of action on the decision process that is being studied. Can we develop more comprehensive models which treat simultaneously the influence of several decision variables (on the part of the firm, competitors, distributors, etc.) on sales and profits?

We believe that the issues listed above are illustrative of the kinds of research that are needed—and will be undertaken—as knowledge about the current state of the art is diffused among many interested groups. In some cases the research will be conducted by university-based research groups and other types of nonprofit institutions. In other instances the type of research needed can only be performed by research groups in business firms dealing with data and problems from the real marketplace.

FUTURE TRENDS IN APPLYING QUANTITATIVE TECHNIQUES

With regard to specific research areas, we believe that future research will be devoted, to an increasing extent, to:

1. *Sequential, adaptive models*—extensions of statistical decision theory and mathematical programming to deal with dynamic, multistage problems under uncertainty.

2. *Gaming and interactive models*—increased efforts to model larger, more complex processes where courses of action are interrelated and where nonlinearities predominate.

3. *Investigation of predictive experts and rules of thumb*—increased emphasis on models which include parameter valves estimated by "predictive experts" (and models for validating the experts' predictive accuracy and reliability) and investigation of current rule-of-thumb versus prescriptive procedures in making "optimal" decisions.

4. *Models of search, implementation, and control*—extensions of current evaluative models, to deal with the design, implementation, and control of courses of action.

5. *Behavioral aspects of decision making, cooperation, and conflict*—increased research on the development of behavioral theories of the firm and the relationship of the firm to its environment.

6. *Model validation*—greater efforts devoted to experimental design, on-line simulation, and sequential modification of models.

7. *Total systems simulation*—development of larger models, encompassing all components of the firm's marketing mix.

8. *Joint optimization models*—using modeling techniques which extend to the producer-distributor-customer sequence, in the effort to assign inventory levels, distribution, arrangements, etc., in such a way as to produce lower costs for the *entire* sequence. Such models could be used as a "marketing service" which indicates the the potential gains to be made through mutual cooperation of producer, distributor, and consumer.

9. *Study of model optimality in interactive systems*—investigation of the properties of "optimal" models when competitors employ similar techniques and interaction is present.

10. *Multidimensional scaling techniques*—use of psychometric and linguistic models in the study of consumers' perceptions of alternative brands and the manner in which preferences are formed.

11. *Taxonomic techniques*—use of the techniques of numerical taxonomy such as cluster analysis and hierarchical grouping procedures as a means for developing empirical-based classificity systems to describe various phenomena such as brand loyalty and market concentration.[2]

This list, while not exclusive or exhaustive, does suggest an increasing need to model larger, interactive systems composed of relationships that to a large extent are behavioral. If our "forecasts" are borne out, it seems clear that existing data collection and computational procedures will likewise undergo marked changes.

Data Collection Procedures

With growing emphasis on the study of larger systems, present data banks will need to be substantially enlarged and modified. Much attention has been given lately to so-called "marketing intelligence" systems [3] that embrace many of the data requirements which have been discussed in earlier chapters.

Lipstein envisions that in the next twenty years computerized information storage and retrieval systems will be commonplace in the advertising agency business.[4] Not only will media and standard service data be stored in these systems, but historical advertising campaign data (for both the firm and its competitors) will be part of the data bank. The media re-

[2] Adapted from Paul E. Green, "Marketing Theory and the Literature of the Management Sciences," in Michael H. Halbert, *The Meaning and Sources of Marketing Theory* (New York: McGraw-Hill Book Company, 1965), p. 136.

[3] William T. Kelley, "Marketing Intelligence for Top Management," *Journal of Marketing*, XXIX (October 1965), 19–24.

[4] Benjamin Lipstein, "Propects for the Management Sciences in Marketing," a paper presented at the American meeting of The Institute of Management Sciences, Dallas, Texas, February 1966.

search man, for example, will have available continuously updated rates for each medium and basic data on reach, frequency, and the demographic and socioeconomic characteristics of the medium's audience as input to a media simulator for testing alternative allocations of media expenditures.

The tabulation and analysis of standard research questionnaires will be fully automated, and the results will be stored in computer files. In addition, store audit techniques will probably undergo substantial change as consumer purchases are recorded on cash-register computers, ultimately to become input data for market simulators. Lipstein speculates that even the "creative" process of advertising copy preparation may be aided by using a computer to search for interesting combinations of appeals from information on customer awareness, preferences, and brand-switching characteristics, in a manner not unlike that in which engineers already use computers to design production equipment, bridges, and, indeed, other computers.

If some of these predictions sound farfetched, it is significant to note that market simulators already exist,[5] although, of course, not on the scale envisioned by Lipstein. And, the use of central computers with satellite consoles is already a reality. We would speculate that corporate marketing departments will likewise develop data systems, simulators, and the like on a scale comparable to that forecasted for advertising agencies. One of the major advantages of attempts to develop *explicit* models of marketing systems is that attention is focused on the appropriate data that must be obtained in order to make the models operational. For example, some of the recent work in adaptive models [6] suggests that promotional effectiveness models will have built into them a mechanism for specifying not only "optimal" current promotional expenditures but also the field experiments to be conducted in order to keep the model updated for future periods.

Data Processing

Hand in hand with the gathering of data goes the manipulation, summarization, and analysis associated with converting it into usable form for both researcher and manager. Several developments of interest to marketing researchers of the future are already under way. Much progress, for example, has been made in the development of simplified languages with which the user can communicate with the machine. A variety of algebraic and simulation languages have already been developed, and it is to be expected that considerable advances will be made along these lines.

[5] See *Simulmatics Media-Mix: Technical Description* (New York: The Simulmatics Corporation, October 1962).

[6] John D. C. Little, "A Model of Adaptive Control of Promotional Spending," *Operations Research*, XIV (November–December 1966), 1075–91.

Information display devices have long passed the curiosity stage. Automatic plotters and various display devices are currently a reality. In behavioral experiments, for example, the researcher can record subjects' responses directly onto computer tape. Moreover, experimental programs already exist which enable the researcher to "test out" various hypotheses on the data by merely using a console to key in various instructions for maximum flexibility in data manipulation.

Research in large probabilistic information-processing systems is also a current reality. Edwards and Phillips, for example, have been exploring the possibilities of developing such a system for the continuous updating of military intelligence.[7] Human experts supply data inputs to a master console, and the likelihood of various hypotheses about adversaries' courses of action is continuously updated from intelligence reports. Extensions of this approach (which utilizes Bayesian decision theory) to business intelligence systems are not only possible, but likely.

In all probability, business accounting systems also will be modified to take into account such concepts as opportunity costs (penalties associated with the failure to take certain courses of action). One might also speculate, with some justification, that "managers of information" will become part of the top executive elite of the future.

In short, we feel that *current* research activities provide a meaningful basis for making the "prognostications" cited above. Most surely, these developments in technology will affect the theory and practice of marketing analysis in the future.

[7] Ward Edwards and L. D. Phillips, "Man as a Transducer for Probabilities in Bayesian Command and Control Systems," in *Human Judgments and Optimality*, ed. Maynard W. Shelly and Glenn L. Bryan (New York: John Wiley & Sons, Inc., 1964), pp. 360–401.

Selected Readings

Alderson, Wroe, and Stanley Shapiro, *Marketing and the Computer*. Englewood Cliffs, N. J.: Prentice-Hall, Inc., 1962.

Banks, Seymour, *Experimentation in Marketing*. New York: McGraw-Hill Book Company, 1965.

Blalcok, Hubert M., Jr., *Causal Inferences in Nonexperimental Research*. Chapel Hill: University of North Carolina Press, 1964.

Cochran, William G., and Gertrude M. Cox, *Experimental Designs*. New York: John Wiley & Sons, Inc., 1957.

Cox, Donald R., *Planning of Experiments*. New York: John Wiley & Sons, Inc., 1958.

Draper, N. R., and H. Smith, *Applied Regression Analysis*. New York: John Wiley & Sons, Inc., 1966.

Ezekiel, Mordecai, and Karl A. Fox, *Methods of Correlation and Regression Analysis*. New York: John Wiley & Sons, Inc., 1959.

Federer, Walter T., *Experimental Design*. New York: The Macmillan Company, 1955.

Forrester, Jay W., *Industrial Dynamics*. Cambridge, Mass.: The M.I.T. Press and New York: John Wiley and Sons, Inc., 1961.

Frank, Ronald E., Alfred A. Kuehn, and William F. Massy, *Quantitative Techniques in Marketing Analysis*. Homewood, Ill.: Richard D. Irwin, Inc., 1962.

Green, Paul E., and Donald S. Tull, *Research for Marketing Decisions*. Englewood Cliffs, N. J.: Prentice-Hall, Inc., 1966.

Morrison, Donald F., *Multivariate Statistical Methods*. New York: McGraw-Hill Book Company, 1967.

Orcutt, Guy C., Martin Greenberger, Janice Korbel, and Alice Rivlin, *Micro-Analysis of Socioeconomic Systems: A Simulation Study*. New York: Harper and Brothers, 1961.

Schlaifer, Robert, *Probability and Statistics for Business Decisions*. New York: McGraw-Hill Book Company, 1959.

Zeisel, Hans, *Say It With Figures*. New York: Harper & Row, Publishers, 1957.

Index